Workbook

Small Gas Engines

fundamentals ♦ service ♦ troubleshooting ♦ repair ♦ applications

by

Alfred C. Roth
Professor Emeritus, College of Technology
Eastern Michigan University
Ypsilanti, Michigan

Publisher
The Goodheart-Willcox Company, Inc.
Tinley Park, Illinois

International Standard Book Number 1-56637-575-4
3 4 5 6 7 8 9 10 00 03 02 01

Important Safety Notice

Proper service and repair is important to the safe, reliable operation of small gas engines and related equipment. Procedures recommended and described in the text are effective methods of performing service operations. The textbook also contains various safety procedures and cautions that must be followed to minimize the risk of personal injury and part damage. These notices and cautions are not exhaustive. Those performing a given service procedure or using a particular tool must first determine that safety is not being jeopardized.

Engine illustrations on the front and back covers courtesy of Briggs & Stratton Corporation; Generac Corporation; Kawasaki Motor Corporation, U.S.A.; and Mercury Marine.

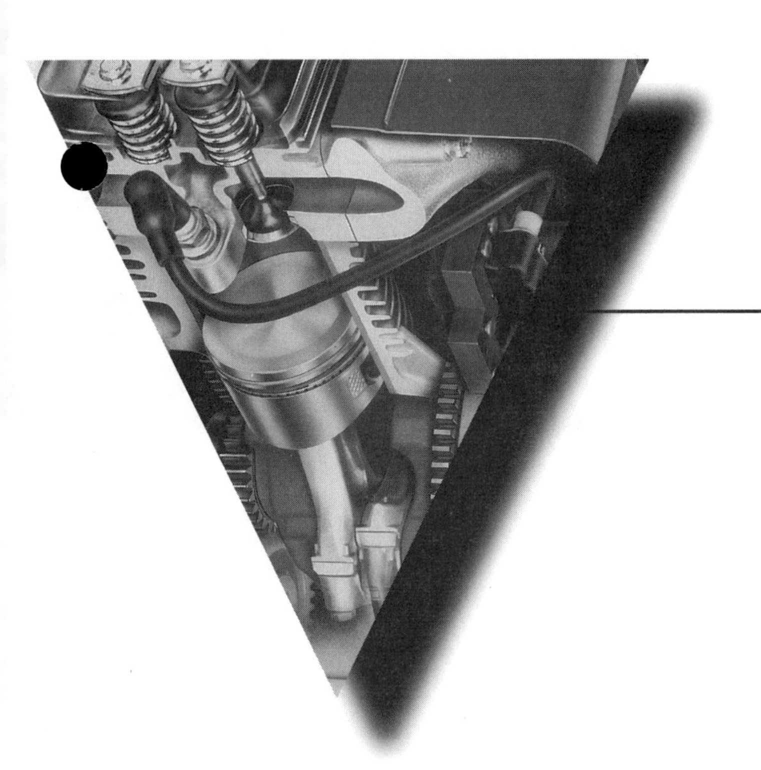

Introduction

This *Workbook* is designed for use with the text, ***Small Gas Engines***. As you complete the questions and problems in this *Workbook,* you can review the facts and concepts presented in the text.

The *Workbook* chapters correspond to the chapters in the text. After reading your assignment in the text, do your best to complete these questions and problems carefully and accurately.

Each chapter of the *Workbook* includes objectives and instructions. Several types of questions and problems are given in each chapter. The various types of questions include matching, identification, multiple choice, fill-in-the-blank, and written answer. Also included in the *Workbook* are a number of *Jobs* on pages 155–218, and sample Outdoor Power Equipment (OPE) tests on pages 219–223.

You may want to learn about small gas engines for several reasons. You may need consumer and general maintenance information, or you may be interested in the problems of mechanics, engine design, engine testing, production methods, or sales and servicing. The study of the ***Small Gas Engines*** text and *Workbook* will help you understand engine construction and basic operating principles.

Contents

		Workbook	Text
Chapter 1	Safety in the Small Gas Engine Shop	7	13
Chapter 2	Tools and Measuring Instruments	11	21
Chapter 3	Fasteners, Sealants, and Gaskets	19	43
Chapter 4	Engine Construction and Principles of Operation	25	63
Chapter 5	Two-Cycle and Four-Cycle Engines	33	77
Chapter 6	Measuring Engine Performance	39	91
Chapter 7	Fuel and Emission Control Systems	45	109
Chapter 8	Carburetion	51	123
Chapter 9	Ignition Systems	59	147
Chapter 10	Lubrication Systems	69	175
Chapter 11	Cooling Systems	73	191
Chapter 12	Preventive Maintenance and Troubleshooting	77	201
Chapter 13	Fuel System Service	83	217
Chapter 14	Ignition System Service	89	239
Chapter 15	Engine Inspection, Disassembly, and Cylinder Reconditioning	97	271
Chapter 16	Piston and Piston Ring Service	101	281
Chapter 17	Bearing, Crankshaft, Valve, and Camshaft Service	107	297
Chapter 18	Lawn Equipment	115	331
Chapter 19	Lawn and Garden Tractors	123	365
Chapter 20	Snow Throwers	133	403
Chapter 21	Personal Watercraft	139	425
Chapter 22	Career Opportunities and Certification	151	463

Jobs

1—Shop Safety 157
2—Hand Tool Identification and Use 163
3—Four-Cycle Engine Disassembly 167
4—Two-Cycle Engine Disassembly 171
5—Measuring Instruments 175
6—Cleaning, Inspecting, and Measuring Engine Parts 179
7—Four-Cycle Engine Reassembly 189
8—Two-Cycle Engine Reassembly 197
9—General Engine Troubleshooting 201
10—Ignition System Service 205
11—Fuel System Service 215
OPE Sample Certification Tests 219

Safety in the Small Gas Engine Shop

Name____

Date ______________________ Period ____________

Instructor____________________________________

After studying this chapter, you will be able to:

▼ Explain why a clean, well-organized shop is extremely important.

▼ List several dangers associated with working in a small engine shop.

▼ Explain the importance of maintaining and using tools properly.

▼ Describe the methods for minimizing the risks involved in working with small engines.

▼ Explain the function of OSHA.

Instructions: After studying Chapter 1 of the text, complete the following questions and problems.

1. Failure to adhere to safety rules in the small gas engine shop could lead to serious _____ or _____. 1. ____________________ ____________________

2. Safety in the small gas engine shop is _____ responsibility. 2. ____________________

3. Gasoline and other flammable liquids give off vapors that can _____ if exposed to heat or flame. 3. ____________________

4. What are three methods that should be used to eliminate fire hazards in the small gas engine shop?

____

____

____

5. Never pour gasoline into the tank of a(n) _____ engine. 5. ____________________

6. Tools that have been used should always be _____ and replaced neatly in a toolbox or workbench storage place. 6. ____________________

7. The highly flammable and explosive gas given off by the batteries used in battery-operated ignition systems and implements is _____. 7. ____________________

8. Why should gasoline *never* be used as a cleaning solvent? ____________________

____

____

9. Battery acid can cause severe _____ when it comes in contact with skin or eyes. 9. ____________________

10. When working with small gas engines, _____ should not be worn. 10. ____________________
    a. loose fitting clothing
    b. jewelry
    c. neckties
    d. All of the above.

11. How can long hair be worn safely when working around engines, implements, and moving machinery?

____

____

12. When working with hazardous chemicals, ____ _____ and safety glasses or goggles should be worn. 12. ____________________

13. Two types of ear/hearing protection that can be worn are _____ and _____. 13. ____________________

____

14. During what three conditions should ear/hearing protection be worn? ____________________

____

____

____

15. To prevent foot and toe injury, _____ _____ should be worn. 15. ____________________

16. Carbon monoxide (CO) is a gas given off when running gasoline engines. Breathing small amounts of carbon monoxide will cause _____ and _____. 16. ____________________

____

17. When running an engine in the shop, what precautions should be taken to avoid inhalation of carbon monoxide fumes? ____________________

____

18. For protection against air contaminants in the shop, a personal air _____ should be worn by the technician. 18. ____________________

19. To prevent injury, it is best to _____ wrenches toward your body. 19. ____________________

20. When using hammers, handles must be in good condition and hammer heads must be _____ so that they do not come off. 20. ____________________

21. Power tools should have all _____ and _____ in place. 21. ____________________

____

Name ____

22. What is the purpose of a "dead man switch" on power tools? ______________________________________

____

____

23. Before making any adjustments to a power tool or machine, you should ____________________________

____

____.

24. Compressed air is very useful in the shop, but it can also be hazardous when improperly used. List several safety rules to follow when using compressed air.

____

____

____

____

____

25. When lifting heavy objects, you should always lift with your _____. 25. ____________________
   a. legs
   b. back
   c. arms
   d. All of the above.

26. _____ is the most common cause of shop fires. 26. ____________________

27. Before using electrical equipment, check wires for _____ or _____. 27. ____________________

____

28. All electrical equipment should be properly grounded or double _____. 28. ____________________

29. Why should circuit breaker switches be labeled? ____

____

____

30. Why should you *never* operate engines at speeds exceeding those recommended by the manufacturer?

____

____

31. When an engine is running, all _____ and _____ should be in place. 31. ____________________

____

32. Engine ignition systems produce voltages as high as _____ volts and can cause electrical shock. 32. ____________________

33. In addition to wearing ear/hearing protection, engines should always be operated with the _____ installed. 33. ____________________

34. All fire extinguishers should be inspected _____.
   a. weekly
   b. yearly
   c. monthly
   d. bimonthly

34. ______________________

35. If there is a gasoline or oil fire in the shop, a Class _____ fire extinguisher should be used to put it out.

35. ______________________

36. Electrical fires are considered Class _____ fires.

36. ______________________

37. Where should the first aid kit be located? ______________________

38. All businesses and industries are required to follow safety regulations established by a governmental organization called _____.

38. ______________________

• Research and write complete answers to the following questions.

39. Explain why safety is so important in the outdoor power equipment industry. ______________________

40. Explain the benefits for a technician who works in a safe, clean, working environment. ______________________

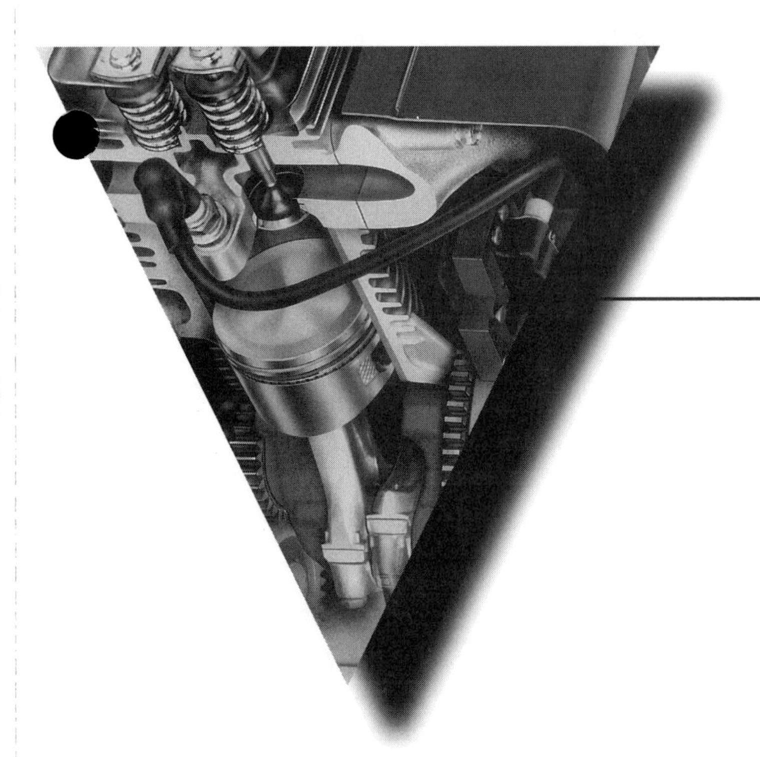

Tools and Measuring Instruments

Name_______________

Date _______________ Period _______________

Instructor_______________

After studying this chapter, you will be able to:

- ▼ Explain why quality tools and measuring instruments should be used when servicing small gas engines.
- ▼ Use common hand tools properly.
- ▼ Summarize the reasons that small engine components must be measured carefully.
- ▼ Demonstrate several of the common measuring techniques.

Instructions: After studying Chapter 2 of the text, complete the following questions and problems.

1. To avoid damaging engine parts you should always use tools _____ for the job.
   1. _______________
2. Some tools are common to many jobs but some are _____ _____ tools designed for specific tasks.
   2. _______________ _______________
3. Identify the wrenches shown below by their proper names.
   3. A. _______________
   B. _______________
   C. _______________
   D. _______________

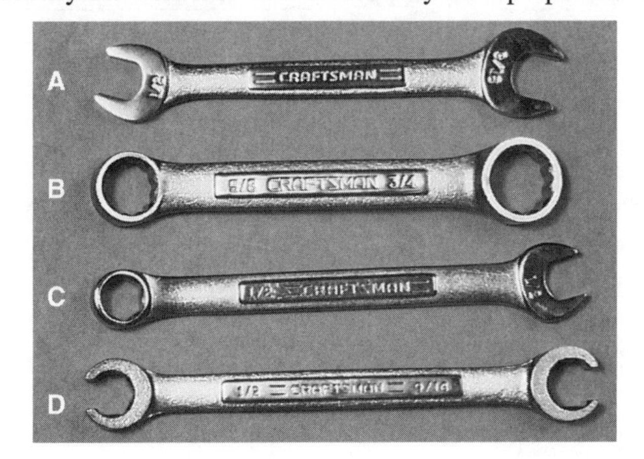

4. A(n) _____ wrench is *least* likely to slip around the head of a bolt. 4. ______________

5. The safest way to use a wrench for loosening or tightening is to _____ it in the direction of rotation. 5. ______________

6. A very useful tool that can save time and reach places where other wrenches *cannot* is the _____ wrench. 6. ______________

7. Fasteners and wrenches are available in both U.S. customary and _____ sizes. 7. ______________

8. Fasteners that are critical and must be reliable and safe are tightened with a(n) _____ wrench. 8. ______________

9. A wrench used for hex-socket head screws is called a(n) _____ wrench. 9. ______________

10. A torque reading is the product of the length of the handle and the _____ _____. 10. ______________

11. Most small engine torque charts provide specified amounts in both _____ pounds and _____ pounds. 11. ______________

12. Identify the types of pliers illustrated below and indicate their common applications.

12. A. ______________

____

B. ______________

____

C. ______________

____

D. ______________

____

13. When using retaining ring pliers, you should always wear _____ _____. 13. ______________

14. When fasteners resist removal due to rust, a(n) _____ oil can be used to assist removal. 14. ______________

15. Screwdrivers are available in a variety of shapes and _____ to fit many kinds of screws. 15. ______________

16. When using screwdrivers, it is essential that the blade fit the _____ properly in the screw. 16. ______________

17. A(n) _____ screwdriver has a pointed, cross-shaped end, which fits screws with cross-shaped recesses in their heads. 17. ______________

18. When using a ball peen hammer, care must be taken not to _____ or _____ parts. 18. ______________

____

19. Ball peen hammer sizes are rated by the _____ of the hammer head. 19. ______________

Name ________________________________

20. _____ is used to make the faces for soft hammers.
    a. Brass
    b. Lead
    c. Plastic or rubber
    d. All of the above.

20. ____________________

21. When drilling a hole, starting the drill can be assisted by using a(n) _____ punch first to make a small depression.

21. ____________________

22. A prick punch has a point angle of _____ and a center punch has a point angle of _____.
    a. 60°, 80°
    b. 60°, 90°
    c. 45°, 90°
    d. 90°, 60°

22. ____________________

23. A cylindrical punch used for driving straight pins, tapered pins, and roll pins is called a(n) _____.

23. ____________________

24. A(n) _____ punch is often used to align holes in mating parts.

24. ____________________

25. A cold chisel for shearing bolts, pins, or rivets should have a cutting edge angle of about _____. For shearing sheet metal, the cutting edge angle should be about _____.
    a. 90°, 60°
    b. 45°, 60°
    c. 60°, 90°
    d. 90°, 45°

25. ____________________
____

26. For shearing bolts or rivets, the cutting edge of a cold chisel should be _____.
    a. curved
    b. straight

26. ____________________

27. When using punches or chisels, _____ _____ or _____ must be worn.

27. ____________________
____

28. When the hammered end of a punch or cold chisel becomes flared or mushroomed, it should be _____ to its original shape.

28. ____________________

29. The tool used to pull a gear from a shaft is called a(n) _____ _____.

29. ____________________

30. When small items are accidentally dropped into small crevices or recesses, _____ and _____ tools can often be used to retrieve them.

30. ____________________
____

31. Identify the parts of the machinist's vise illustrated below.

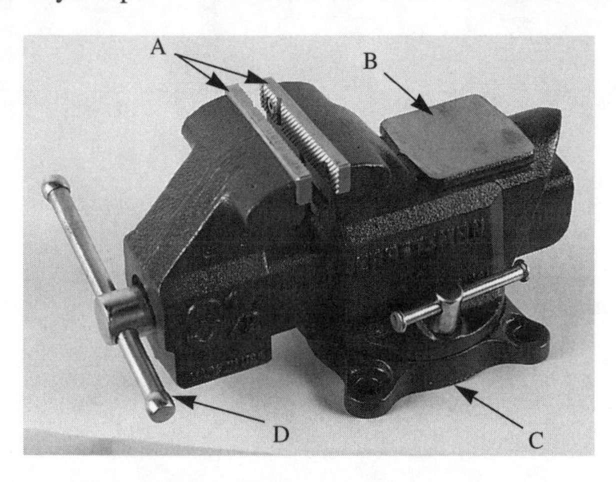

31. A. ____________
B. ____________
C. ____________
D. ____________

32. The jaws of a machinist vise are made from hardened steel and have a rough gripping surface. Delicate parts can be clamped safely in the jaws by using soft _____ _____.

32. ____________

33. When using a vise to hold a part for sawing or filing, the part should be adjusted so the work is done _____ to the vise jaws to minimize vibration.

33. ____________

34. A safety cleaning tank should be filled with a(n) _____, _____ solvent.

34. ____________

35. Some cleaning tanks are equipped with a(n) _____ _____, which automatically closes the lid in case of fire.

35. ____________

36. When servicing small gas engines, accurate measurements must be made to determine whether components are within _____ _____.

36. ____________

37. Label the parts of the micrometer illustrated below.

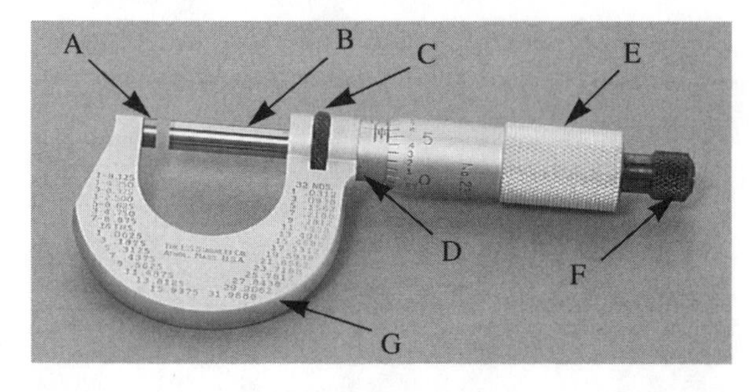

37. A. ____________
B. ____________
C. ____________
D. ____________
E. ____________
F. ____________
G. ____________

38. A(n) _____ micrometer should be used to measure the outside diameter of a piston or valve stem.

38. ____________

39. To measure the diameter of a cylinder, you should use a(n) _____ micrometer.

39. ____________

40. How does temperature affect a micrometer?

____

____

41. Before using a micrometer, it should be tested for proper _____.

41. ____________

Name ____

42. In order to take accurate measurements, a micrometer's _____ and _____ faces must be very clean. — 42. ____________________ ____________________

43. A(n) _____ micrometer should be used for taking measurements in narrow grooves. — 43. ____________________

44. A 0-1″ micrometer can be checked for proper calibration by carefully closing the _____ against the _____ to read zero. — 44. ____________________ ____________________

45. When checking a 1-2″ micrometer for proper calibration, a 1″ cylindrical gauge, gauge _____, or gauge _____ should be used. — 45. ____________________ ____________________

46. If a micrometer is equipped with a ratchet-stop, it should be clicked _____ time(s). — 46. ____________________

47. Many micrometers are equipped with a(n) _____ _____, which keeps the spindle from rotating when the instrument is removed from the part being measured. — 47. ____________________

48. The _____ micrometer is graduated in thousandths of an inch. One one-thousandth of an inch is written in decimal form as _____ inch. — 48. ____________________ ____________________

49. A(n) _____ micrometer is graduated in ten-thousandths of an inch. One ten-thousandth of an inch is written in decimal form as _____ inch. — 49. ____________________ ____________________

50. Each small space on the sleeve of a micrometer represents a distance of _____ an inch. — 50. ____________________

51. Each space on the thimble of the micrometer represents a distance of _____ an inch. — 51. ____________________

52. Assume that the micrometer scales illustrated below are 0-1″ standard micrometers. Read the scales and record your answers in the appropriate blanks. — 52. A. ____________________ B. ____________________ C. ____________________

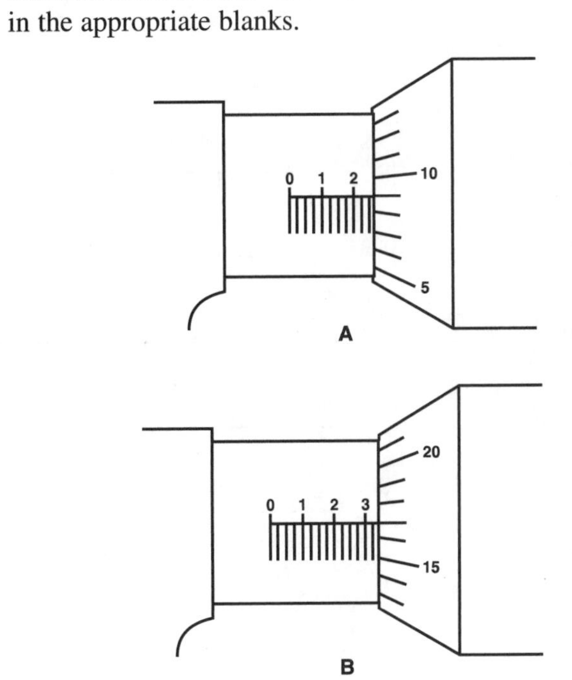

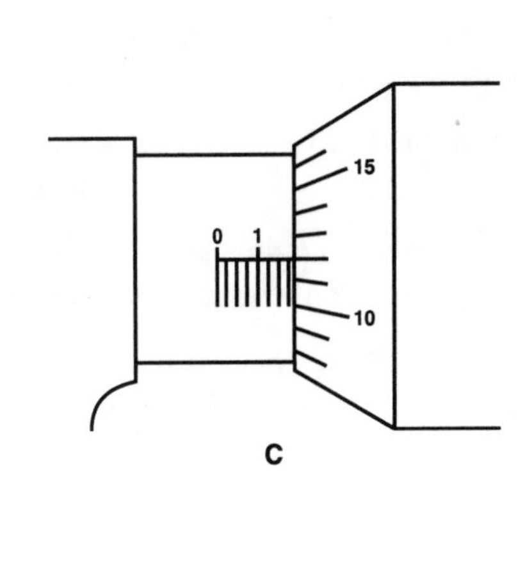

53. Assume that the micrometers illustrated below are 0-1″ Vernier micrometers. Read the scales and record your answers in the appropriate blanks.

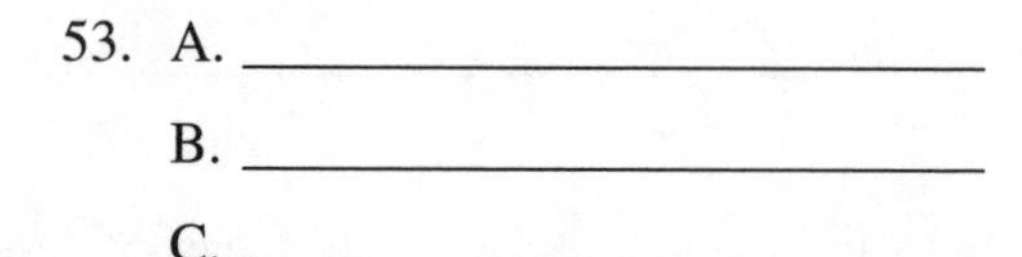
53. A. ______________

B. ______________

C. ______________

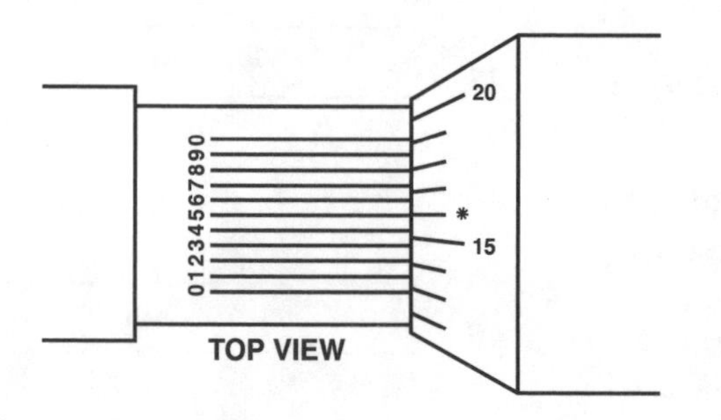

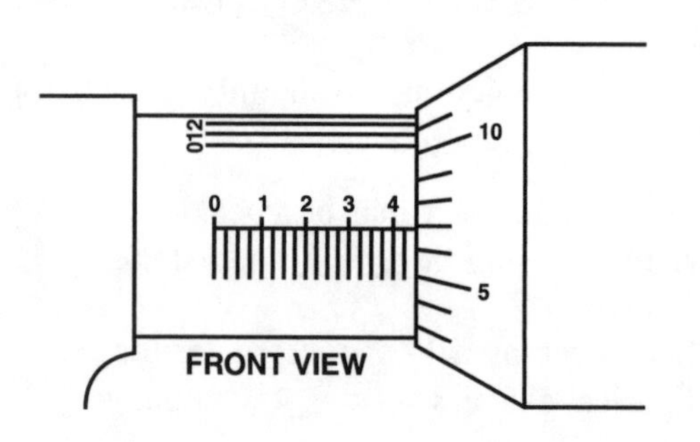

A

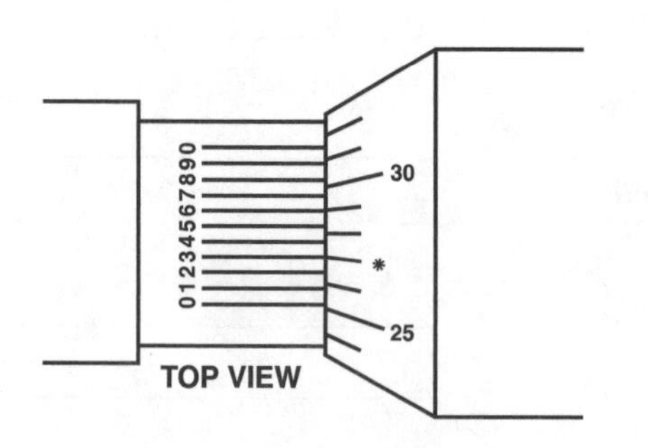

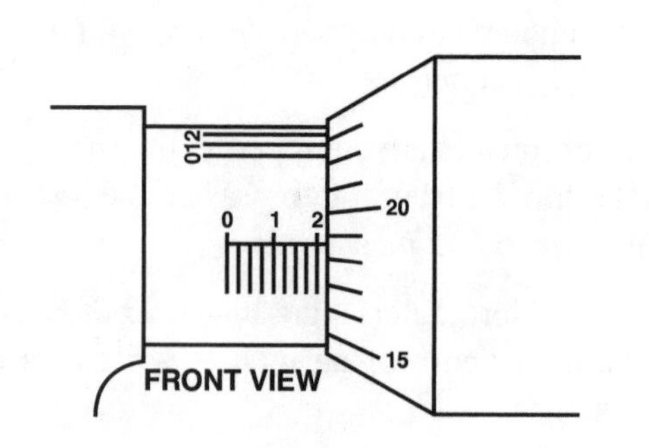

B

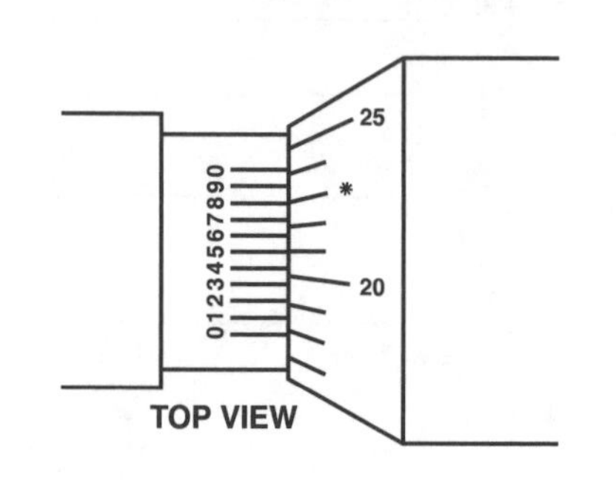

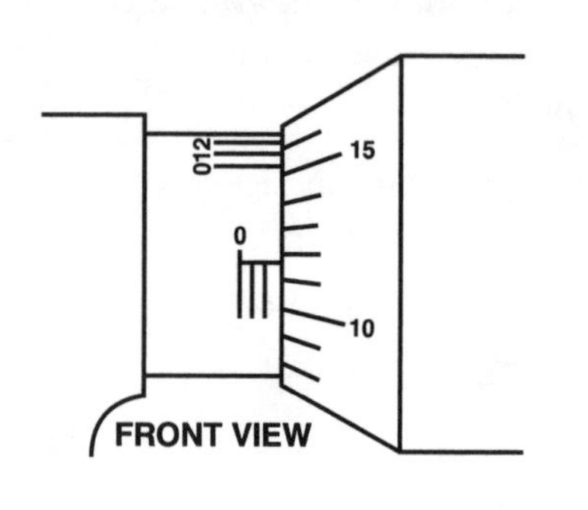

C

54. Modern _____ micrometers make taking measurements quick and easy by displaying decimal readings in a window.

54. ______________

55. Telescoping gauges are often called _____-type instruments because they do not provide direct dimensional readings.

55. ______________

56. To measure an inside dimension with a telescoping gauge, it is also necessary to use a(n) _____ micrometer.

56. ______________

57. When removing a telescoping gauge from a hole or cylinder, it should be _____ to avoid changing the reading.

57. ______________

58. A(n) _____ _____ gauge is used to measure holes that are too small to be measured with a telescoping gauge.

58. ______________

59. Valve stem clearance is commonly measured with a tool called a(n) _____ gauge.

59. ______________

60. The strength of a valve spring is measured with an instrument called a valve spring _____ tester.

60. ______________

Name ____

61. A(n) _____ _____ can be used to verify the length and straightness of a valve spring. — 61. ______________________________

62. Dial indicators can be used to measure part movement. The indicator's _____ can be rotated to locate zero under the needle. — 62. ______________________________

63. An instrument used to determine the number of threads per inch on a bolt, nut, or threaded hole is called a(n) _____ _____ gauge. — 63. ______________________________

64. Screw pitch gauges are available in both standard and _____ threads. — 64. ______________________________

- Research and write a complete answer to the following question.

65. Explain why it is important to take good care of your work tools and instruments.

____

____

____

____

____

____

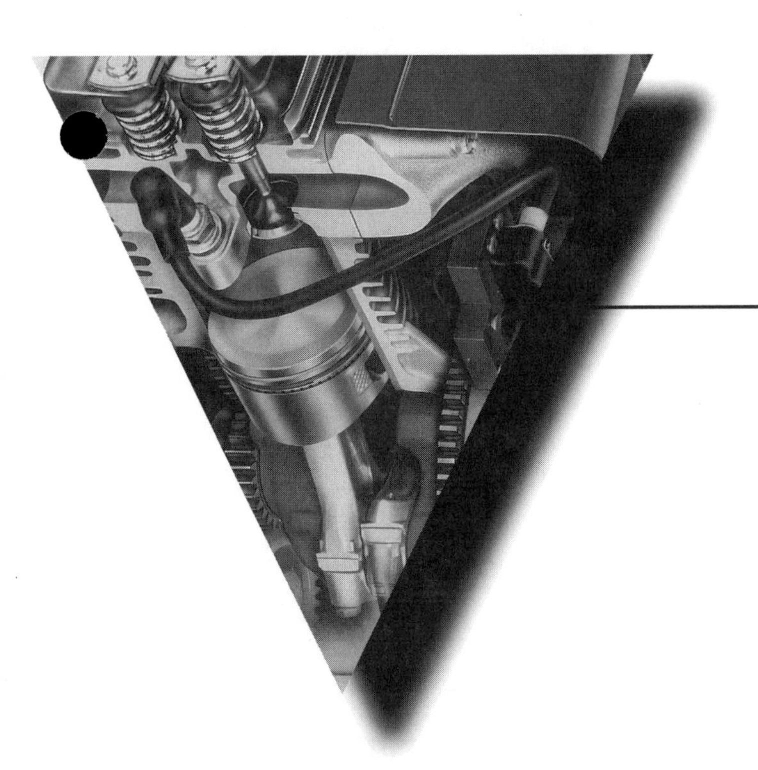

CHAPTER 3

Fasteners, Sealants, and Gaskets

Name______________________________

Date ____________________ Period ____________

Instructor____________________________

After studying this chapter, you will be able to:

- ▼ Identify fasteners used on small gas engines and implements.
- ▼ Remove and install various fasteners correctly.
- ▼ Repair or produce internal and external threads.
- ▼ Properly select and install fasteners.
- ▼ Remove, select, and install gaskets correctly.

Instructions: After studying Chapter 3 of the text, complete the following questions and problems.

1. List at least four of the various conditions to which fasteners are exposed during service.

____

____

____

____

2. A thread is a(n) _____ _____ that circles around a shaft, or in a hole. 2. ______________________

3. Flat head screws or bolts must have their heads set into a(n) _____ hole so they will be flush with the surface. 3. ______________________

4. The most common angle for the heads of flat head screws is _____. 4. ______________________

5. Identify the bolt and screw heads illustrated below.

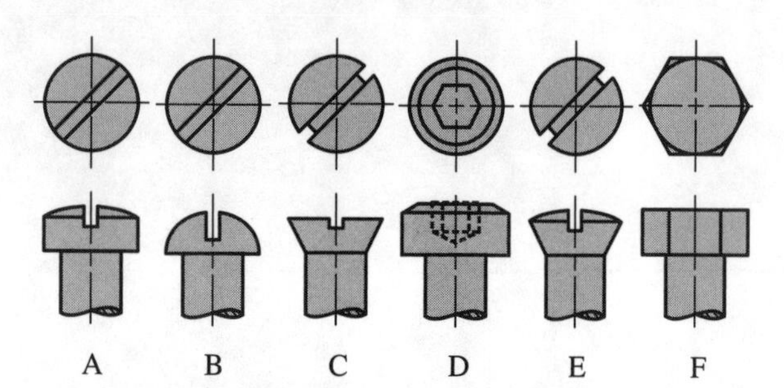

5. A. ____________________
B. ____________________
C. ____________________
D. ____________________
E. ____________________
F. ____________________

6. Identify the set screws illustrated below.

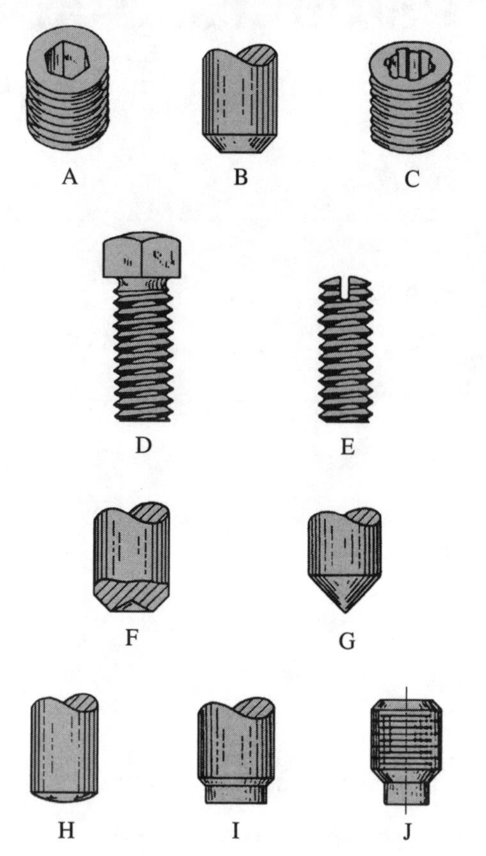

6. A. ____________________
B. ____________________
C. ____________________
D. ____________________
E. ____________________
F. ____________________
G. ____________________
H. ____________________
I. ____________________
J. ____________________

7. When securing a shaft with a set screw, the shaft must have a(n) _____ groove so that the part can easily be removed. 7. ____________________

8. Cutting threads in a hole is a process called _____. 8. ____________________

9. The unthreaded hole that a bolt or screw passes through should have a small amount of _____. 9. ____________________

10. The unthreaded portion of bolt is called the _____. 10. ____________________

11. A larger, smoother clamping surface can be provided for a bolt by adding a(n) _____ _____ under the head. 11. ____________________

Name ________________________________

12. Identify the nuts illustrated below.

A B C

D E F

12. A. ______________________
B. ______________________
C. ______________________
D. ______________________
E. ______________________
F. ______________________

13. When axial clearance is required, such as with some bearings on shafts, a(n) _____ nut and a cotter pin should be used.

13. ______________________

14. A(n) _____ nut can be used when a part is subjected to continuous vibration that might loosen the nut.

14. ______________________

15. Bolt grades relate to the minimum _____ strength of the bolt.

15. ______________________

16. When a bolt reaches its load bearing limit, it begins to _____ and stretch.
    a. crack
    b. weaken
    c. bend
    d. None of the above.

16. ______________________

17. The markings on the heads of bolts are indicators of their _____ and minimum tensile strength.

17. ______________________

18. The largest diameter of a thread is called the _____ diameter.

18. ______________________

19. The number of threads per inch on standard American threads is called the _____ of the thread.
    a. pitch
    b. crest
    c. shank
    d. tensile

19. ______________________

20. The very bottom of a thread is called the _____ and the top is called the _____.

20. ______________________
____

21. A thread with the greatest allowable manufacturing tolerance would be a Class _____ fit.

21. ______________________

22. The fit that is found on most common fasteners is a Class _____.

22. ______________________

23. A thread specified as a 3/8-24 UNF-2A × 1 would be a(n) _____ thread with _____ threads per inch and the fastener is _____ long.

23. ______________________
____
____

24. A thread designated as M-10 × 1.5 × 30 indicates it is _____, its diameter is _____ and the pitch is _____.

24. ______________________

____

____

25. In order to tighten a right hand screw or bolt in a threaded hole it must be turned _____.

25. ______________________

26. If the threads in a hole are damaged they can be recut by a process called _____. This is accomplished with a tool called a tap.

26. ______________________

27. Torque charts, or a small gas engine service manual, will provide proper torque amounts in _____ pounds and/or _____ pounds.

27. ______________________

____

28. The tool used for cutting external threads is a thread _____.

28. ______________________

29. Write the formula in the space below that will provide the desired drill size for tapping a new hole.

29. ______________________

30. The tool that holds a die for cutting external threads is called a(n) _____ _____.

30. ______________________

31. When cutting external threads with a die, it is important that the die be started on the correct side and that a good _____ _____ be used.

31. ______________________

32. Using the tap drill chart on pages 53–54 of the text, determine the correct drill size for making a 3/8-16 UNC-2B thread.

32. ______________________

33. The correct drill size for an M6 × 1 thread is a(n) _____ drill.

33. ______________________

34. When bolting a piece of metal to a piece of wood with the bolt head against the metal, a(n) _____ _____ should be placed between the nut and the wood.

34. ______________________

35. The most commonly used lock washer is the _____ washer made of spring steel with beveled ends.

35. ______________________

36. _____ are used to retain parts in a fixed position, or maintain alignment.
    a. Pins
    b. Bolts
    c. Nails
    d. None of the above.

36. ______________________

Name ______________________________

37. Identify the pins illustrated below.

A B C D E F

37. A. ______________________
B. ______________________
C. ______________________
D. ______________________
E. ______________________
F. ______________________

38. Threaded fasteners can be protected from loosening from vibration by applying a thread _____.

38. ______________________

39. Most sealants are resistant to _____.
  a. water and gasoline
  b. oil and salt
  c. grease
  d. All of the above.

39. ______________________

40. When threads are exposed to constant heating and cooling conditions, they can be kept from being cold welded together through the application of _____ compounds.

40. ______________________

41. Gaskets are used between engine parts to prevent leakage of _____.
  a. engine oil and coolant
  b. vacuum
  c. compression
  d. All of the above.

41. ______________________

42. List the ten rules for properly installing gaskets.

____

____

____

____

____

____

____

____

____

____

• Research and write complete answers to the following questions.

43. Why should head gasket bolts be tightened in a crisscross sequence? ______

44. Explain in some detail why there are so many different kinds of fasteners and fastener accessories. Describe the kinds of forces to which fasteners are often exposed. ______

45. Describe why it is so important to torque critical fasteners to specific tightness. What can occur if bolts are not torqued properly? Explain ductility, hardness, temper, and tensile and yield strength. ______

Engine Construction and Principles of Operation

Name________________________

Date ______________ Period ________

Instructor______________________

After studying this chapter, you will be able to:

- ▼ Explain simple engine operation.
- ▼ List the qualities of gasoline that make it an efficient fuel for small engines.
- ▼ Explain why gasoline is atomized in the small engine.
- ▼ Identify the basic components of a small engine and describe the function of each part.

Instructions: After studying Chapter 4 of the text, complete the following questions and problems.

1. A gasoline engine is a mechanism that transforms _____ energy into _____ energy for doing useful work. 1. ______________ ______________
2. A gasoline engine is an internal _____ engine. 2. ______________
3. In an internal combustion engine, the gasoline is combined with _____ and burned inside the engine. 3. ______________
4. One end of the connecting rod is fastened to the piston. The other end is fastened to an offset _____, or ____ of the crankshaft. 4. ______________ ______________
5. The space above the piston where the combustible mixture burns is called the _____ chamber. 5. ______________
6. The force applied to the piston is a result of the ________________________ ________________________.
7. Burned gases are released through a(n) _____ _____ following the power stroke of the piston. 7. ______________

8. As burned gases are released, a fresh _____-_____ charge enters the cylinder, and the momentum of the power stroke turns the crankshaft journal through bottom dead center (BDC) and into the upstroke on another power cycle.

8. ______________________

9. Name the parts of the engine shown below.

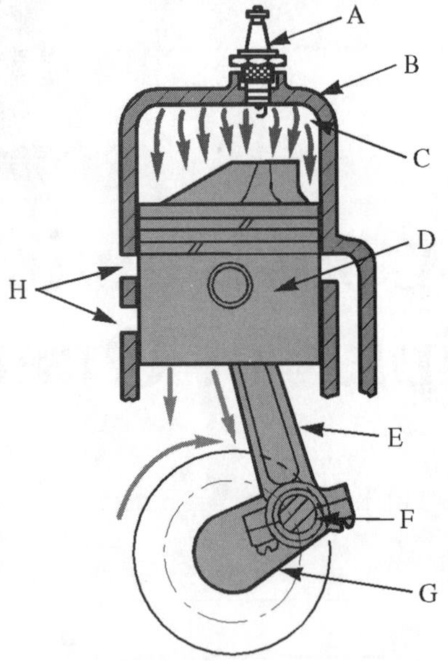

A
B
C
D
E
F
G
H

9. A. ______________________
B. ______________________
C. ______________________
D. ______________________
E. ______________________
F. ______________________
G. ______________________
H. ______________________

10. Gasoline is a petroleum product that is mainly a mixture of _____ and _____.

10. ______________________
____

11. Explain why we should conserve gasoline and use it wisely.______________________
____

12. List three desirable characteristics of gasoline for use in engines.

____
____
____
____

13. An engine with a relatively high compression should use gasoline that has a _____.
   a. high octane and burns fast
   b. low octane and burns slow
   c. high octane and burns slow
   d. low octane and burns fast

13. ______________________

14. In order to expose more surface area of the fuel to create rapid burning, the fuel is broken into very small droplets and mixed with air. This process is called _____.

14. ______________________

15. To perform useful work, the explosive force caused by burning gas must be _____ and _____.

15. ______________________
____

Name ______________________________

16. List four major parts of an elementary engine.

____

____

____

____

17. List and briefly describe five basic areas of engine operation.

____

____

____

____

____

18. The _____ keeps all other parts of the engine in proper alignment.
    a. gaskets
    b. cylinder block
    c. connecting rod
    d. None of the above.

18. ______________________________

19. Cooling efficiency of air-cooled engines is improved through the use of _____ _____.

19. ______________________________

20. Cylinder blocks for small engines are usually made of _____ or a(n) _____ alloy.

20. ______________________________

____

21. Why are aluminum cylinder blocks cast around a steel sleeve? ______________________________

____

____

22. The cylinder block must be rigid and strong enough to contain the _____ developed by the expanding gases.

22. ______________________________

23. Identify the parts indicated on the figure below.

23. A. ______________________________
    B. ______________________________
    C. ______________________________
    D. ______________________________
    E. ______________________________

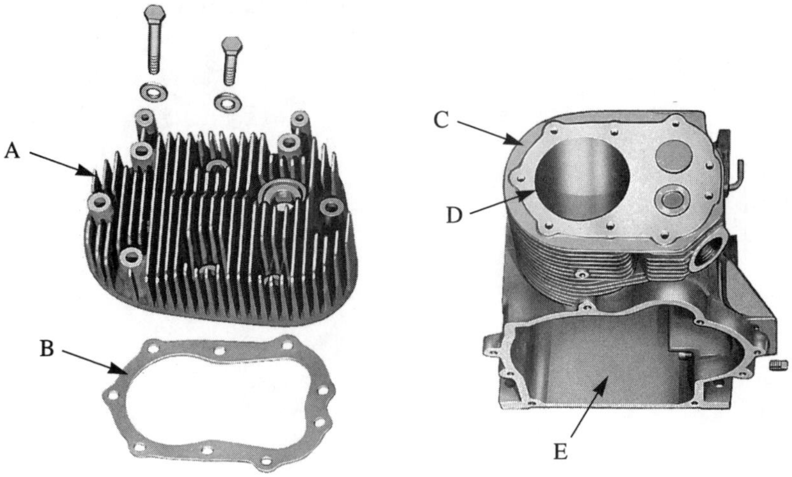

A

B

C

D

E

24. The _____ is the major rotating part of the engine. 24. ______________________

25. Why is a woodruff key used to prevent the flywheel from turning on the crankshaft? ______________________

____

____

26. Crankshafts for small engines are generally made from _____ steel. 26. ______________________

27. The flywheel end of the crankshaft is _____ to fit the hole in the flywheel. 27. ______________________

28. To reduce vibration during operation, the crankshaft has _____ to equal the weight of the _____ _____. 28. ______________________

____

29. The crankcase must be rigid and strong enough to withstand the _____ forces of the crankshaft, while keeping all parts in proper alignment. 29. ______________________

30. _____ and _____ are used to prevent oil leakage from the crankcase. 30. ______________________

____

31. Identify the parts indicated on the valve train illustrated below.

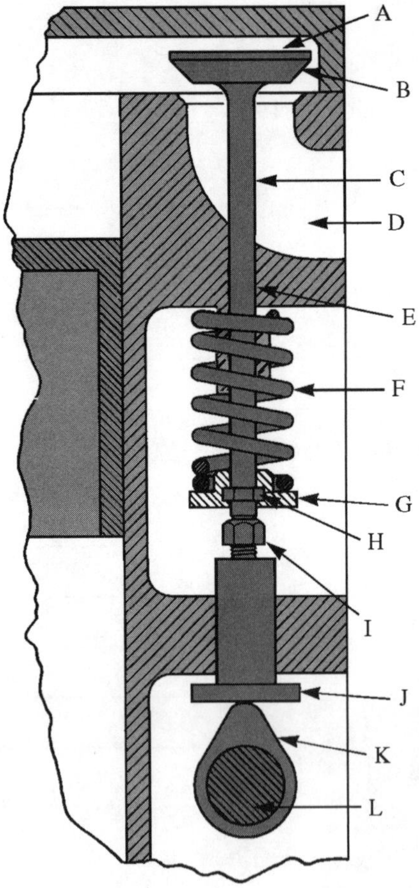

31. A. ______________________

B. ______________________

C. ______________________

D. ______________________

E. ______________________

F. ______________________

G. ______________________

H. ______________________

I. ______________________

J. ______________________

K. ______________________

L. ______________________

Name ______________________________

32. The _____ is the straight line driving member of the engine. 32. ______________

33. The piston provides a(n) _____ between the combustion chamber and the crankcase. 33. ______________

34. Properly installed piston rings _____. 34. ______________
    a. prevent blow-by of exhaust gases into the crankcase
    b. prevent leakage of oil into the combustion chamber
    c. fit the grooves near the top of the piston with a slight side clearance
    d. All of the above.

35. The piston is hollow to reduce _____. 35. ______________

36. The sliding piston is connected to the rotating crankshaft with a metal link called a(n) _____. 36. ______________

37. Expanding _____ push the piston toward the crankshaft, causing the connecting rod to turn the shaft. 37. ______________

38. Identify the intake port and the exhaust port in the figure below. Draw arrows to indicate the flow of the air-fuel mixture. 38. A. ______________
    B. ______________

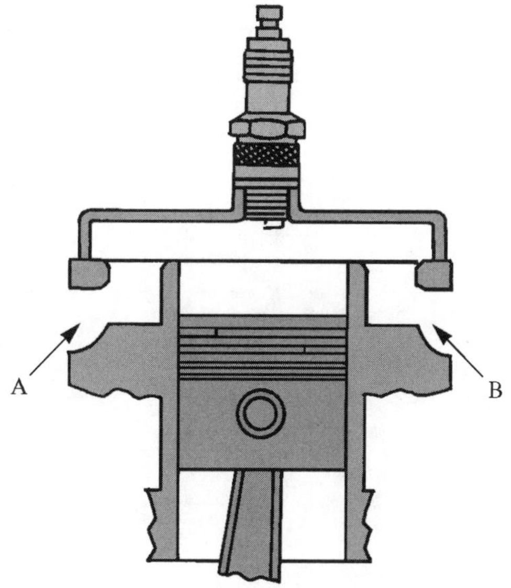

39. Both valves are closed during the period of the _____. 39. ______________
    a. expansion of the burning gases
    b. intake of air
    c. exhaustion of the burned gases
    d. None of the above.

40. How are valves kept in alignment? ______________________________

____

____

41. Intake and exhaust ports are sealed with _____ valves. 41. ______________

42. What is the purpose of the spring keeper and washer? ____________________

____

43. What is the purpose of the camshaft? ____________________

____

44. Why are valve lifters used? ____________________

____

45. The camshaft timing gear is always _____ as the crankshaft gear. 45. __________
    a. the same size
    b. twice as large
    c. three times as large
    d. four times as large

46. During assembly, _____ _____ on the camshaft gear and crankshaft gear must be matched. 46. __________

47. List three functions of the flywheel.

____

____

____

____

____

48. Identify the parts indicated in the figure below.

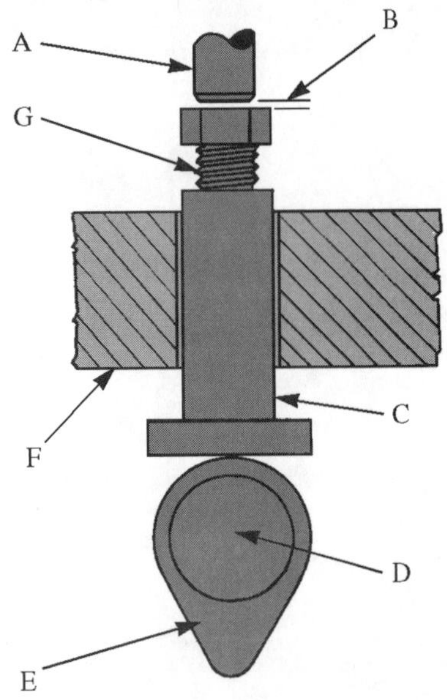

48. A. __________
B. __________
C. __________
D. __________
E. __________
F. __________
G. __________

Name ____________________________________

49. Identify the parts indicated in the figure below.

49. A. ____________________________
    B. ____________________________
    C. ____________________________

• Research and write a complete answer to the following question.

50. After studying Chapter 4, write in your own words how an engine works by describing the function of each of its basic parts. ____

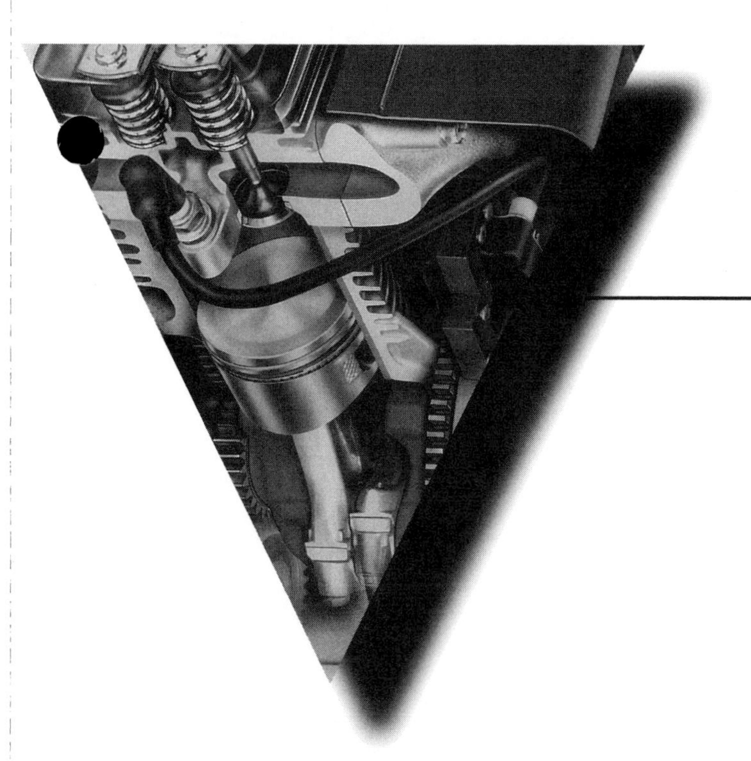

Two-Cycle and Four-Cycle Engines

Name______________________________

Date ____________________ Period ___________

Instructor_________________________

After studying this chapter, you will be able to:

▼ Describe four-stroke cycle engine operation and explain the purpose of each stroke.
▼ Explain the concept of valve timing.
▼ Compare the lubrication system in a four-cycle engine to the system in a two-cycle engine.
▼ Describe two-stroke cycle engine operation and explain the principles of two-cycle operation.
▼ List the advantages and disadvantages of two-cycle and four-cycle engines.

Instructions: After studying Chapter 5 of the text, complete the following questions and problems.

1. A basic engine feature that identifies an engine type is the number of _____ required to complete one operating/power cycle. 1. ____________________

2. The sequence of strokes in a four-stroke cycle engine beginning with the intake stroke is _____. 2. ____________________
   a. compression, power, and exhaust
   b. power, compression, and exhaust
   c. exhaust, power, and compression
   d. None of the above.

3. Both valves are closed during the _____ and _____ strokes. 3. ____________________
   ____

4. List three key functions performed by the intake valve.
   ____
   ____
   ____
   ____

5. Why do intake valves usually last longer than exhaust valves? ______________________________

____

____

6. How does the compression stroke increase the force of combustion? Give two reasons.

____

____

____

____

____

____

____

____

____

7. At what point in the power stroke do most engines ignite the air-fuel mixture? _______________

____

____

____

8. If the compression ratio is too high, the fuel may be heated to its flash point and _____ too early. 8. ______________________

9. The process of exhausting the burned gases from the cylinder is called _____. 9. ______________________

10. The exhaust valve may be exposed to pressure as high as _____ pounds per square inch. 10. ______________________

11. With arrows, indicate the paths of heat transfer while the exhaust valve is closed.

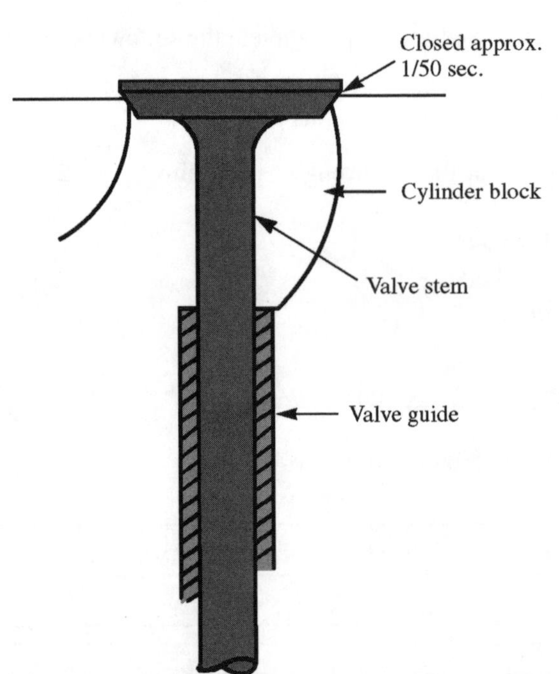

Name ______________________________

12. What is shown in the figure below? ______________________________
____
____

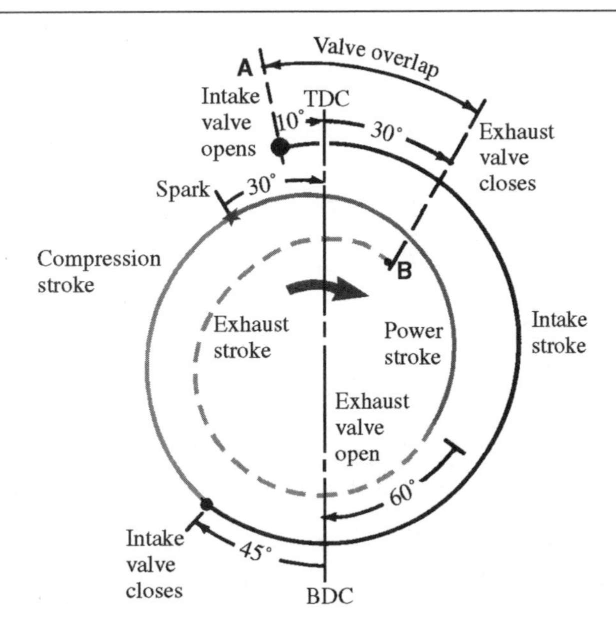

13. Explain valve overlap and its purpose. ______________________________
____
____

14. Explain why the intake valve does not close until after bottom dead center. ______________________________
____

15. How does a technician know that the valves are timed properly? ______________________________
____
____

16. The two most common lubricating systems used on small engines are the _____ system and the _____ system.

16. ______________________________
____

17. Identify the parts of the lubrication system shown below.

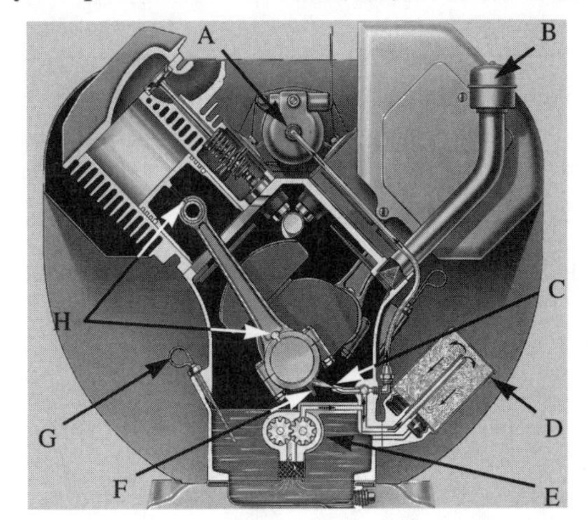

17. A. ______________________________
B. ______________________________
C. ______________________________
D. ______________________________
E. ______________________________
F. ______________________________
G. ______________________________
H. ______________________________

18. The two-cycle engine produces a power stroke on every _____.
    A. two revolutions, while a four-cycle engine produces a power stroke on every four revolutions
    B. revolution, while a four-cycle engine produces a power stroke on every four revolutions
    C. stroke, while a four-cycle engine produces a power stroke on every two strokes
    D. revolution, while a four-cycle engine produces a power stroke on every two revolutions

18. ____________________

19. Explain how lubrication is provided for a two-cycle engine as compared to a four-cycle engine. __________

____

____

____

20. Explain why two-cycle engines can be used in all positions. ____________________

____

____

21. Why is more oil required to operate a two-cycle engine than a four-cycle engine? ____________________

____

22. The valve system on cross-scavenged engines is usually either the _____ valve type, or _____ valve type.

22. ____________________

____

23. Loop-scavenged engines have the transfer ports located _____ the exhaust port.
    a. 180° to
    b. 90° to
    c. directly across from
    d. 15° to

23. ____________________

24. The _____-_____ two-cycle engine type has a contoured baffle on top of the piston to direct the air-fuel mixture upward into the cylinder while exhaust gases are being expelled.

24. ____________________

25. The transfer port on a two-cycle engine directs the air-fuel mixture from the _____ to the _____.

25. ____________________

____

26. Explain how the air-fuel mixture enters the two-cycle engine. ____________________

____

____

27. Explain how the air-fuel mixture moves from the crankcase to the cylinder. ____________________

____

____

28. Reed valves are closed by crankcase _____ and opened by _____ pressure.

28. ____________________

____

Name ____

29. Identify the parts of the reed valve in the figure below.

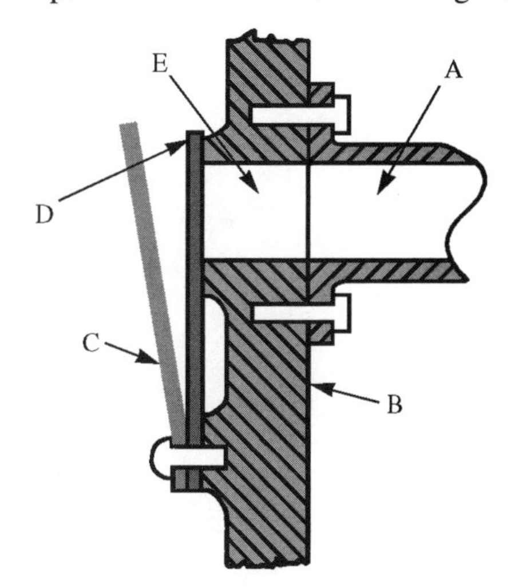

29. A. ____________________
B. ____________________
C. ____________________
D. ____________________
E. ____________________

30. In the figure below, draw arrows to show the intended direction of air-fuel mixture flow through the reed valve.

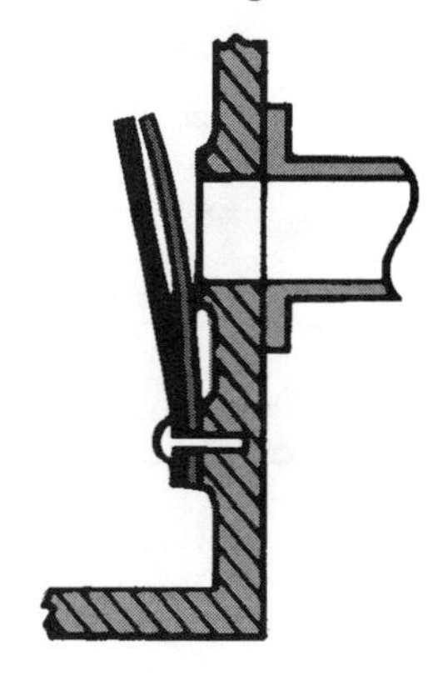

31. _____ is created when air and fuel molecules are compressed together.

31. ____________________

32. _____ _____ prevent leakage of compression past the piston.

32. ____________________

33. One power cycle of a four-stroke engine requires the crankshaft to rotate _____.
    a. one-half revolution
    b. one revolution
    c. two revolutions
    d. four revolutions

33. ____________________

34. What two things determine the amount of power produced during the power stroke? ____________________

____

35. The hottest part of the exhaust valve is the _____. The major portion of the heat is transferred from the valve through the _____.
   a. head, valve seat
   b. valve seat, head

35. ______________________

____

36. During the compression stroke, ignition occurs when the piston is _____ dead center.
   a. at top
   b. before top
   c. after top
   d. before bottom

36. ______________________

37. What are three key functions of an intake valve?

____

____

____

38. _____ pressure forces air through the carburetor.

38. ______________________

• Research and write complete answers to the following questions.

39. Explain the complete sequence of events that takes place when a four-stroke cycle engine goes through two revolutions beginning with the intake stroke. ______________________

____

____

____

____

____

____

____

____

40. Explain the complete sequence of events that takes place when a two-stroke cycle engine goes through one revolution beginning with the power stroke. ______________________

____

____

____

____

____

____

____

____

____

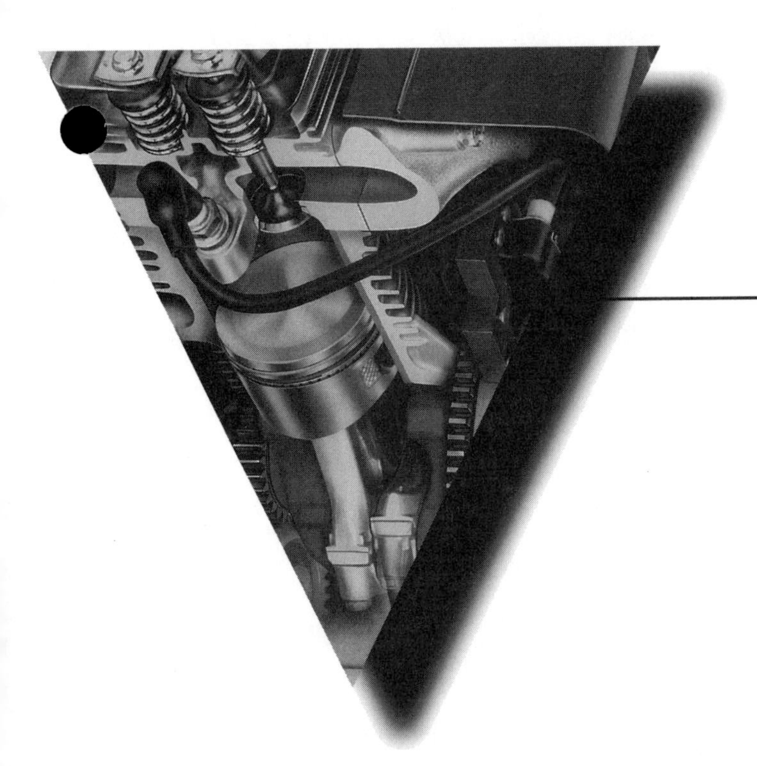

Measuring Engine Performance

Name_______________

Date _______________ Period _______________

Instructor_______________

After studying this chapter, you will be able to:

- Define engine performance.
- Define and compute bore, stroke, displacement, compression ratio, force, work, power, energy, and horsepower.
- Differentiate between the various types of horsepower.
- Explain the function of a Prony brake and a dynamometer.
- Define and calculate torque.
- Explain volumetric efficiency, practical efficiency, mechanical efficiency, and thermal efficiency.

Instructions: After studying Chapter 6 of the text, complete the following questions and problems.

1. Crank _____ is the distance from the centerline of the connecting rod journal to the centerline of the crankshaft. 1. _______________
2. _____ is a force per given unit of area. 2. _______________
3. A measurement of the work an engine does and how well it does the work is called _____. 3. _______________
4. Engine _____ is the diameter or width across the top of the cylinder. 4. _______________
5. _____ is the up or down movement of the piston. 5. _______________
6. When an engine is referred to as *over square*, the _____ is greater than the _____. 6. _______________ _______________
   a. stroke, bore
   b. bore, stroke

7. How well an engine breathes, or draws the air-fuel mixture into the cylinder is referred to as its _____ efficiency.

7. ________________________

8. Calculate the following engine displacements with the information given. Show your work in the space provided.

	Bore	Stroke	Cylinder	Total Displacement
A.	1.378	1.142	1	? cubic inches
B.	2.940	2.750	2	? cubic inches
C.	3.250	2.880	4	? cubic inches

8. A. ________________________

B. ________________________

C. ________________________

9. Define compression ratio for an engine. ________________________

____

____

____

10. If two engines have the same piston diameters, but Engine A has a 6:1 compression ratio, while Engine B has a 5:1 compression ratio, which engine has the longer stroke?
    a. Engine A
    b. Engine B

10. ________________________

11. What is the total force applied to the face of the following pistons? Show your work in the space provided.

	Diameter	Pressure	Total Force
A.	.875″	135 psi	? lb.
B.	2.250″	125 psi	? lb.
C.	3.500″	120 psi	? lb.

11. A. ________________________

B. ________________________

C. ________________________

12. If a total force of 275 lb. is applied to a piston diameter of 2″, what is the pressure? Show your work in the space provided.

12. ________________________ psi

Name ________________________________

13. If a man weighing 170 lb. walks up 12 steps, each step having a rise of 6″, how much work as been done when he reaches the top step? (Show your work in the space provided.)

13. ____________________ ft-lb

14. Compute the leverage as it applies to the figure below. (Show your work in the space provided.)

    Leverage = __?__ lb

14. ____________________

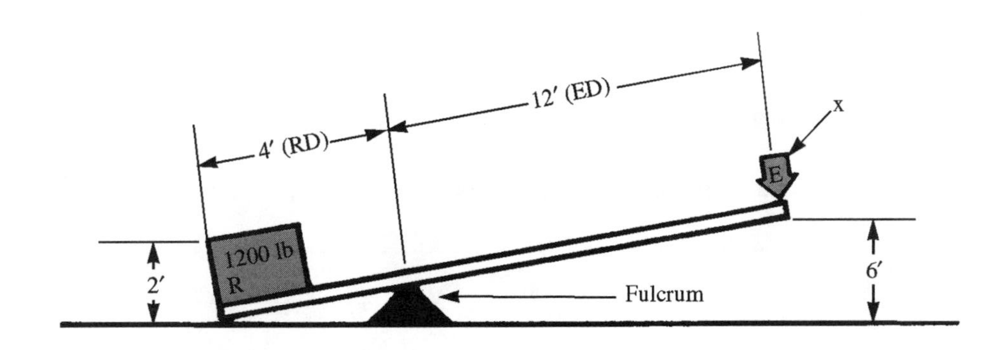

15. If a 3000 lb automobile is lifted to a height of 6′ on a hoist and it takes 30 seconds to do it, how much power has been expended to do the work? Show your work in the space provided.
    A. foot-pounds per second
    B. horsepower

15. A. ____________________
    B. ____________________

16. Identify the kind of energy (potential, kinetic, mechanical, chemical, or thermal) produced by the following sources.
    A. Moving truck
    B. Gasoline
    C. Balloon bursting
    D. Coal burning
    E. Water behind a dam

16. A. ____________________
    B. ____________________
    C. ____________________
    D. ____________________
    E. ____________________

17. Identify the type of horsepower (indicated, frictional, rated, or corrected) described below.
    A. Effect on horsepower by atmospheric conditions
    B. Power developed by burning fuel inside a cylinder
    C. Horsepower recommended for best efficiency
    D. Horsepower lost due to parts rubbing together

17. A. ______________________
    B. ______________________
    C. ______________________
    D. ______________________

18. Determine the indicated horsepower of the following single cylinder, four-cycle engine at 2500 rpm using the PLANK formula. (Show your work in the space provided.)
    mep = 110 psi
    stroke = 2.88″
    bore = 3.25″
    indicated horsepower (ihp) = __?__

18. ______________________

19. List three atmospheric conditions that will cause a decrease in engine horsepower.

____

____

____

20. List five nonatmospheric conditions that can reduce horsepower.

____

____

____

____

____

21. Find the corrected horsepower for the following engine test conditions. Refer to the charts in Figures 6-20 and 6-21 in the text. (Show your work in the space provided.)

21. ______________________

	Test Condition	Correction Factor
Air temperature	80°F	1.02
Barometric pressure	27.7 in Hg	1.10
Wet bulb temperature	68°F	1.0074
Dynamometer horsepower	8.2	_____

Name ____

22. What is the torque being generated if a dynamometer shows a rotational resistance of 125 pounds at a distance of two feet? (Show your work in the space provided.)

22. ________________________ lb ft

23. As engine rpm increases, torque _____.
    a. increases up to a point, then decreases
    b. decreases and then increases to peak rpm
    c. is constant to peak rpm
    d. increases to peak rpm

23. ____________________________

24. Volumetric efficiency can be improved by _____.
    a. altering cam timing
    b. using a larger intake valve
    c. improving exhaust flow
    d. All of the above.

24. ____________________________

25. _____ horsepower is the horsepower at which an engine can be operated continuously without damage.

25. ____________________________

26. _____ efficiency takes into consideration power losses caused by friction, incomplete burning of the air-fuel mixture, heat loss, etc.

26. ____________________________

27. The percentage of power developed in the cylinder (indicated horsepower) compared with that which is actually delivered at the crankshaft (brake horsepower) is called _____ efficiency.

27. ____________________________

28. Thermal efficiency for gasoline engines varies from one engine to another, but is generally about _____.
    a. 10%
    b. 25%
    c. 45%
    d. 60%

28. ____________________________

• Research and write complete answers to the following questions.

29. Explain how and why temperature and barometric pressure affect engine horsepower. ________________

____

____

____

30. What happens to the air-fuel mixture ratio when the altitude (in this case, elevation) is increased? How can the effect be corrected? ____

____

____

____

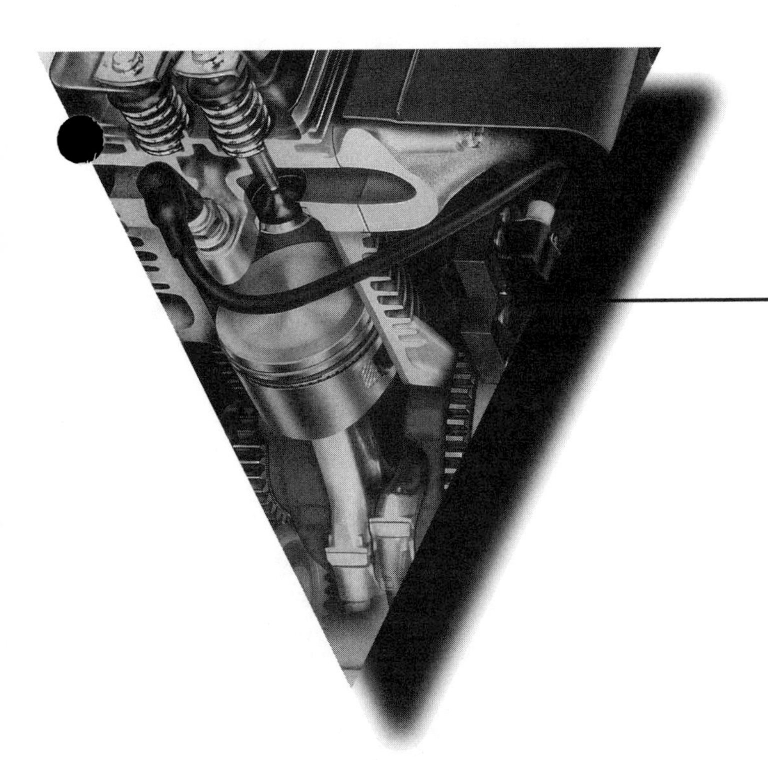

Fuel and Emission Control Systems

Name____

Date ______________________ Period ____________

Instructor_____________________________________

After studying this chapter, you will be able to:

- ▼ Name various types of fuel that can be used in a small engine and list practical applications for each.
- ▼ Explain the importance of proper fuel-oil mixture in a two-cycle engine.
- ▼ Describe the purpose of fuel filters.
- ▼ Explain fuel pump operation.
- ▼ Describe the operation of a pressurized fuel system.
- ▼ Explain the importance of emission control.

Instructions: After studying Chapter 7 of the text, complete the following questions and problems.

1. _____ is the most popular of all small gas engine fuels. 1. ________________________
   a. Gasoline
   b. Liquefied petroleum gas
   c. Natural gas
   d. Kerosene
   e. Diesel fuel

2. Most small gasoline engines run on _____ grade gasoline with an octane rating around _____. 2. ________________________
   ____

3. Explain why gasoline should *not* be stored for long periods of time. ____________________________
   ____
   ____

4. Because of less noxious fumes, _____ engines are often used in places such as warehouses and factories. 4. ________________________

5. LPG burns _____ (faster, slower) than gasoline and has higher ignition temperatures. 5. ________________

6. Due to higher ignition temperatures of LPG, _____ (hotter, colder) spark plugs may be needed. 6. ________________

7. Name the parts of the LP-Gas fuel system shown below. 7. A. ________________
B. ________________
C. ________________
D. ________________
E. ________________

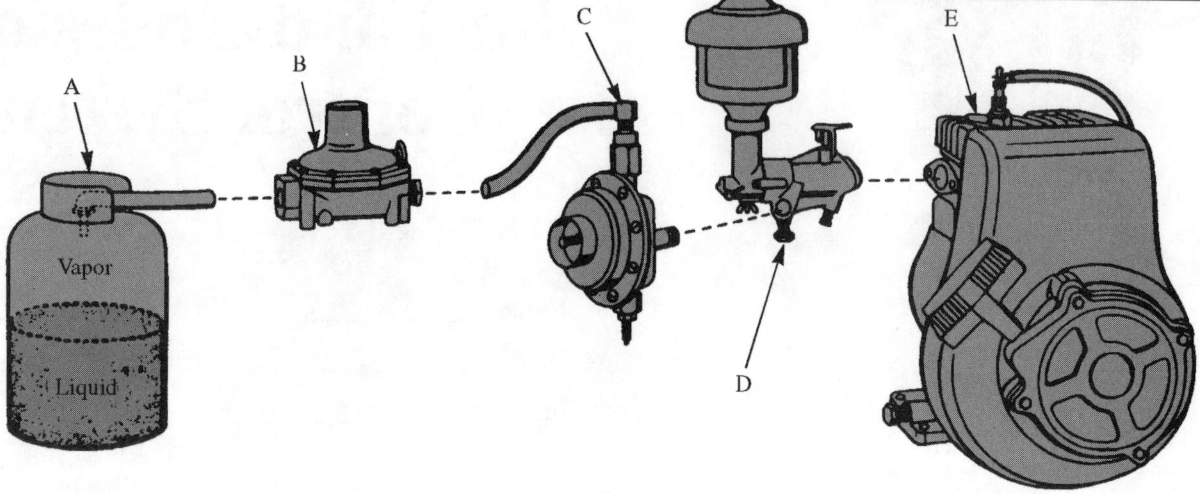

8. List five advantages of an LPG fuel system.

____
____
____
____
____

9. List three disadvantages of an LPG fuel system.

____
____
____

10. Some non-diesel small engines can be converted to operate on kerosene or fuel oil through the installation of a _____ (low, high) compression cylinder head and a special carburetor. 10. ________________

11. True diesel engines may have compression ratios as high as _____ to 1. 11. ________________

12. Most small two-cycle engines are lubricated by a mixture of oil and gasoline. The correct quantity and quality of oil is specified by the _____ specifications. 12. ________________

Name ____

13. Excessive oil in a two-cycle engine fuel mixture can result in _____. 13. ____________________
    a. the rapid buildup of carbon
    b. incomplete combustion
    c. fouling of the spark plugs
    d. All of the above.

14. Fuel tanks must be vented to _____ in the tank. 14. ____________________
    a. increase the vacuum
    b. prevent a vacuum
    c. maintain a vacuum
    d. None of the above.

15. A filler cap with a screw vent should be closed _____. 15. ____________________
    a. at all times
    b. when the engine is under a heavy load
    c. when the engine is not in use
    d. None of the above.

16. Flexible fuel lines in fuel tanks are used on such vehicles as _____ or ______ so that the line will always be where the fuel is deepest in the tank when the vehicle is at a steep angle. 16. ____________________ ____________________

17. Identify the parts indicated on the fuel tank illustrated below. 17. A. ____________________ B. ____________________ C. ____________________ D. ____________________

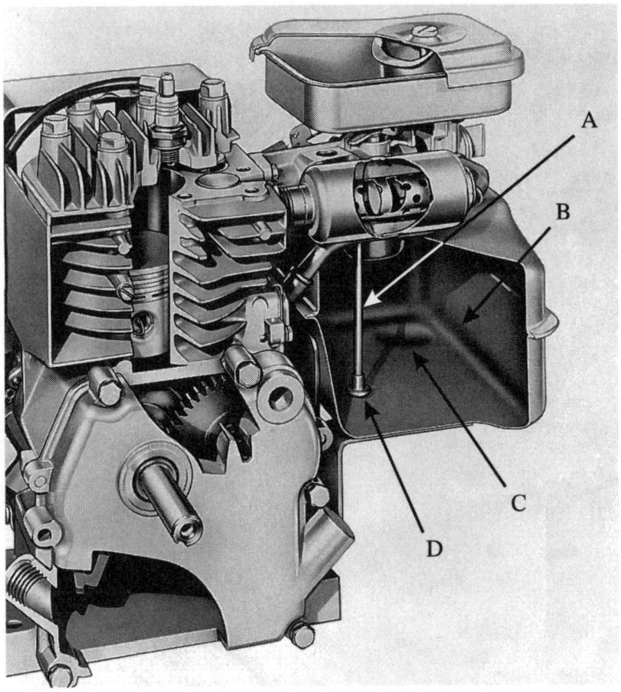

A
B
C
D

18. When is a fuel pump most likely to be used on an engine? ____

____

19. Fuel pumps are designed to provide fuel to the carburetor at a(n) _____ pressure. 19. ____________________

20. Using arrows, show the flow of fuel through the fuel pump illustrated below.

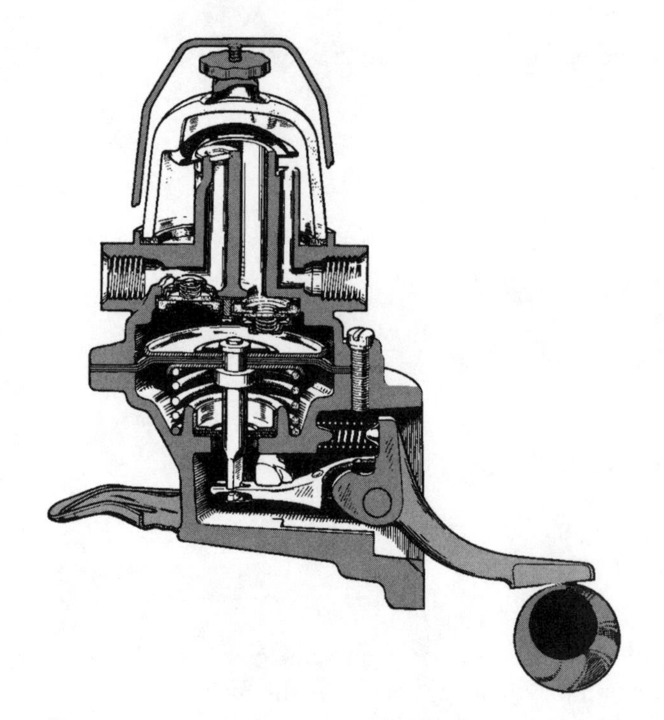

21. A fuel pump hand primer is for use _____.
    a. with pumps that do not have a filter system
    b. when the carburetor float bowl or pump bowl has become empty
    c. with mechanical fuel pumps only
    d. None of the above.

21. ____________________

22. One type of diaphragm fuel pump sometimes used on small gas engines is activated by the pulsing _____ in the intake manifold or crankcase.

22. ____________________

23. A(n) _____ fuel system is used when fuel tanks are located at a considerable distance below the carburetor.

23. ____________________

24. If the temperature of the air around or inside a carburetor becomes high enough to vaporize the gasoline, pockets of vapor will stop all flow of fuel. This is known as _____.

24. ____________________

25. In a(n) _____ _____ fuel system, any vapor that forms is directed back into the fuel tank where the pressure is vented into the atmosphere.

25. ____________________

26. Stricter exhaust emission standards for small gasoline engines will be in place by the year _____.

26. ____________________

27. The new regulations took effect in California and were to be met by manufacturers by _____.

27. ____________________

28. Manufacturers can use any method of design to meet the standards as long as they do not compromise _____.

28. ____________________

29. Small gasoline engines are contributors to _____ and _____ _____ levels in the atmosphere.

29. ____________________

____

Name ______________________________

30. In addition to exhaust emissions from small engines, fuel _____ also contributes to the environmental and health problem. 30. ____________________

31. _____ gallons of gasoline are estimated to be spilled by Americans every summer while refueling and using lawn and garden equipment. 31. ____________________

32. The Phase 1 Small Engine Rule should reduce hydrocarbon emissions from small engines by _____% and CO by _____% when complete fleet turnover occurs. 32. ____________________
____

- Research and write complete answers to the following questions.

33. What is proposed to be done about reducing environmental pollution from lawn and garden equipment?

____
____
____
____
____
____
____

34. How can the residential consumer help to keep evaporative and exhaust emissions minimal? ____________

____
____
____
____
____
____
____

35. What has the small engine and implement industry done to control emissions? What more can they do?

____
____
____
____
____
____
____

Carburetion

Name________________________

Date ______________ Period ________

Instructor________________________

After studying this chapter, you will be able to:

- List and explain the principles of carburetion.
- Identify the three basic types of carburetors.
- Explain float-type carburetor operation.
- Explain the operation of the diaphragm-type carburetors.
- Define manual throttle controls.
- List the basic functions of a governor.
- Adjust and maintain common governors.
- Describe the purpose of an air cleaner.

Instructions: After studying Chapter 8 in the text, answer the following questions and problems.

1. A carburetor's primary function is to mix proper proportions of _____ and _____ to operate the engine. 1. ____________ ____________
2. Gasoline must be _____ by the carburetor. 2. ____________
3. The usual normal air-fuel mixture is a ratio of _____ part(s) of air to _____ part(s) of fuel. 3. ____________ ____________
4. An absolute _____ is any area completely free of air or atmospheric pressure. 4. ____________
5. As soon as the intake valve opens or the intake port is uncovered in a gas engine, _____ _____ forces air through the carburetor and manifold to fill that vacuum. 5. ____________

6. Explain what is occurring in the figure below.

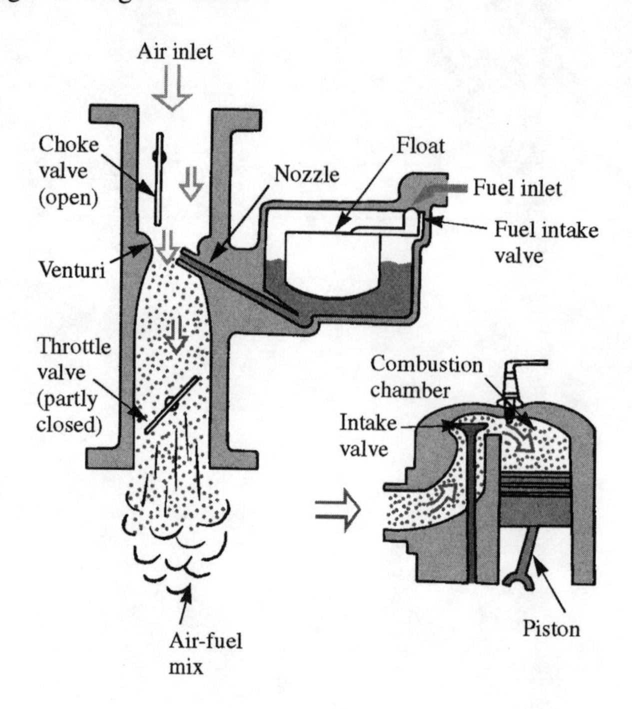

____

____

____

____

____

7. Explain the venturi principle. ____

____

____

____

8. Identify each of the basic types of carburetors shown below.

8. A. _______________

B. _______________

C. _______________

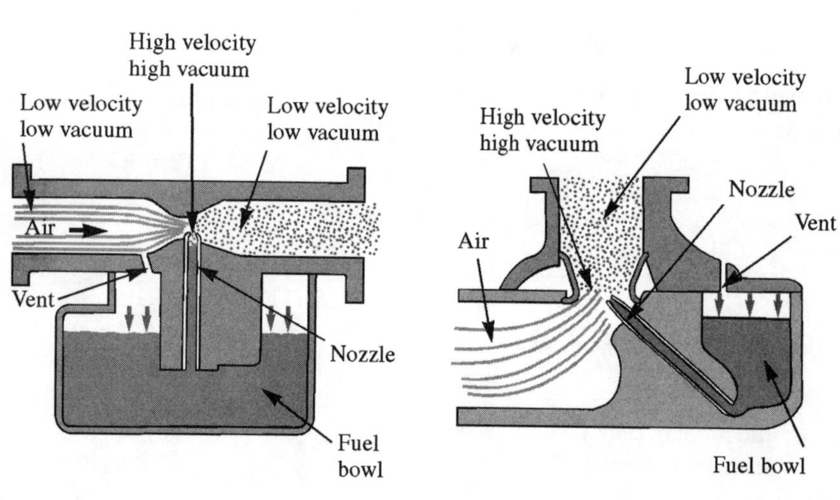

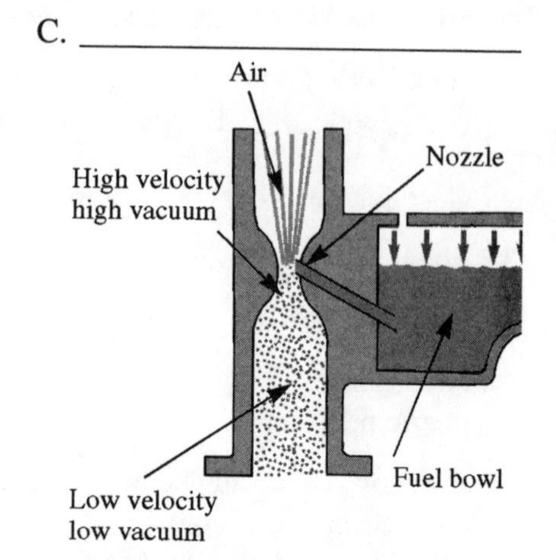

Name ______________________________________

9. Air velocity must be highest in the _____ carburetor. 9. ______________________
   a. natural draft
   b. updraft
   c. downdraft

10. The ______ carburetor can provide larger volumes of fuel for high speed and power requirements. 10. ______________________
    a. natural draft
    b. updraft
    c. downdraft

11. What is the purpose of the carburetor float? ______________________________________

    ____

12. As fuel is used from the float bowl, the float lowers and unseats a(n) _____ valve which lets fuel enter the bowl. 12. ______________________

13. A(n) _____ in the float bowl is used to equalize the air pressure above the fuel in the float bowl and the air pressure entering the carburetor. 13. ______________________

14. The carburetor _____ is a round disc mounted on a shaft located at the intake end of the carburetor. 14. ______________________

15. When closed, the choke provides a _____ (leaner, richer) air-fuel mixture needed during the starting of a cold engine. 15. ______________________

16. Explain your answer to question #15. ______________________________________

    ____

17. Explain the main purpose of the throttle valve. ______________________________________

    ____

18. Explain how the throttle valve controls engine speed and power. ______________________

    ____

    ____

    ____

19. The acceleration _____ stores fuel for use during rapid acceleration. 19. ______________________

20. The economizer circuit is designed to retard fuel flow to the engine at _____. 20. ______________________
    a. idle
    b. full throttle
    c. part throttle
    d. acceleration

21. The primer on a float-type carburetor pumps _____. 21. ______________________
    a. raw fuel through the idle jets
    b. air and fuel through the air bleed jet
    c. air pressure into the float bowl forcing fuel up the nozzle
    d. fuel through main and idle jets

Use the drawings below to answer questions 22 through 24.

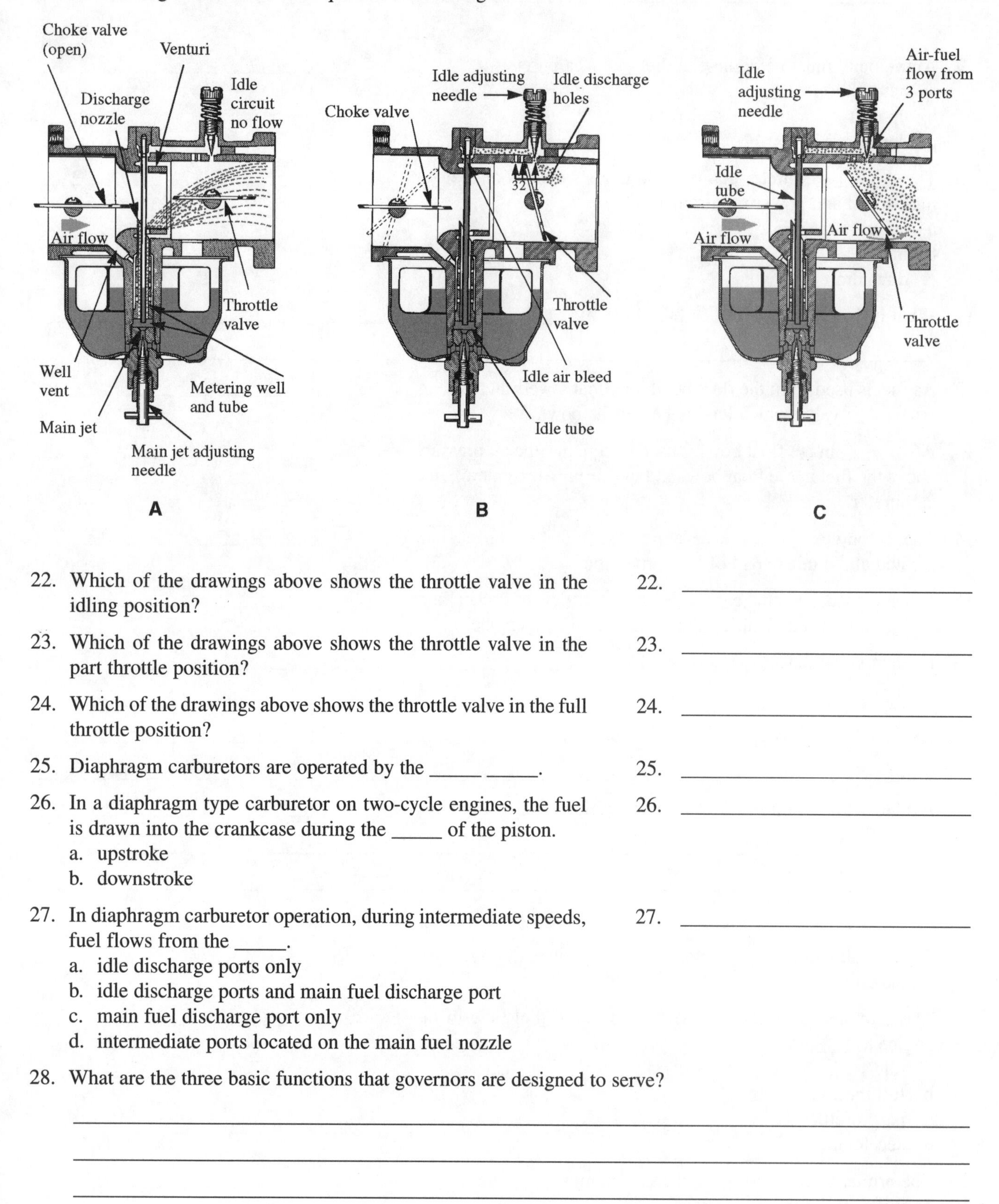

22. Which of the drawings above shows the throttle valve in the idling position? 22. _______________

23. Which of the drawings above shows the throttle valve in the part throttle position? 23. _______________

24. Which of the drawings above shows the throttle valve in the full throttle position? 24. _______________

25. Diaphragm carburetors are operated by the _____ _____. 25. _______________

26. In a diaphragm type carburetor on two-cycle engines, the fuel is drawn into the crankcase during the _____ of the piston. 26. _______________
    a. upstroke
    b. downstroke

27. In diaphragm carburetor operation, during intermediate speeds, fuel flows from the _____. 27. _______________
    a. idle discharge ports only
    b. idle discharge ports and main fuel discharge port
    c. main fuel discharge port only
    d. intermediate ports located on the main fuel nozzle

28. What are the three basic functions that governors are designed to serve?

____

____

____

Name ____

29. List the three types of governors discussed in the text.

 ____

 ____

 ____

30. The air vane governor is operated by the stream of air created by the _____ cooling fins. — 30. ____________________

31. If an engine is designed to run at a constant speed, the speed is adjusted with the governor _____. — 31. ____________________

32. On an air vane governor, controlling speed is accomplished by balancing air pressure with _____ _____. — 32. ____________________

33. Identify the parts in the variable speed air vane governor shown below. — 33. A. ____________________ B. ____________________ C. ____________________ D. ____________________

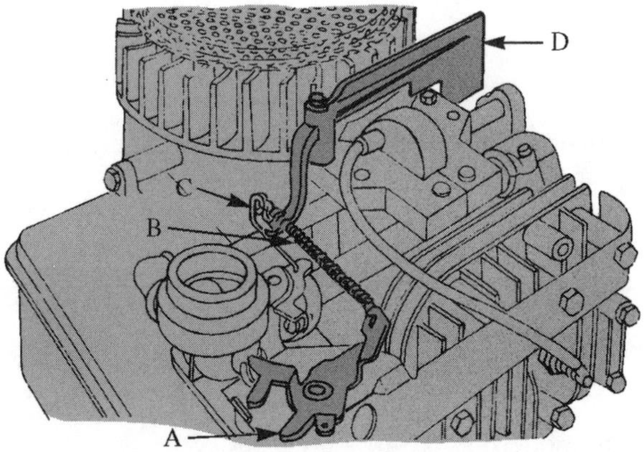

34. Centrifugal governor _____ is when the engine speeds up and slows down repeatedly under a constant load condition. — 34. ____________________

35. A(n) _____ type governor is usually used on farm and industrial engines. — 35. ____________________

36. The ability of a governor to maintain a preset speed without fluctuating is called _____. — 36. ____________________

37. Since blade tip speed is a function of blade length and engine rpm, _____ blades require _____ engine speeds. — 37. ____________________
    a. shorter, lower
    b. longer, lower
    c. longer, higher

38. The percent of engine speed change required to produce a corrective movement of the fuel control mechanism is called _____. — 38. ____________________

39. List three types of air cleaners widely used in small gasoline engines.

____

____

____

40. A(n) _____ _____ type of air cleaner element can be used again by washing it in soapy water. 40. _______________

41. _____ type air cleaners pass the airstream through treated paper, felt, fiber, or flocked screen. 41. _______________

42. As the air filter fills with dirt, the air-fuel mixture will _____. 42. _______________
    a. become leaner
    b. become richer
    c. not change
    d. overspeed the engine

43. When the air filter becomes dirty, the engine will _____. 43. _______________
    a. use more fuel
    b. lose power
    c. accumulate carbon
    d. All of the above.

44. For average applications such as normal yard lawnmowing, the air cleaner should be cleaned every _____ hours, or _____ time(s) per season. 44. _______________

____

45. Most dry type air filter elements _____. 45. _______________
    a. can be washed and re-used indefinitely
    b. must be discarded and replaced with a new filter
    c. can be cleaned by tapping to dislodge light dirt

46. The air filter that is similar to air filters used in modern automobiles is the _____ paper type. 46. _______________

47. When an engine is designed for use in greater than normal dusty/dirty conditions, a(n) _____ element air filter is installed. 47. _______________

48. An engine air cleaner should be examined _____. 48. _______________
    a. every time the engine is serviced or repaired
    b. only when the engine is overhauled
    c. when the engine begins to smoke
    d. every day the engine is used

• Research and write complete answers to the following questions.

49. Describe how the carburetion system accommodates the varying speeds and conditions required of an engine. Include the types and functions of governors. _______________

____

____

____

____

____

____

50. Explain the effects of continuous operation of an engine with a dirty air filter. How can it affect the condition and life of an engine? ____

30. [illegible]

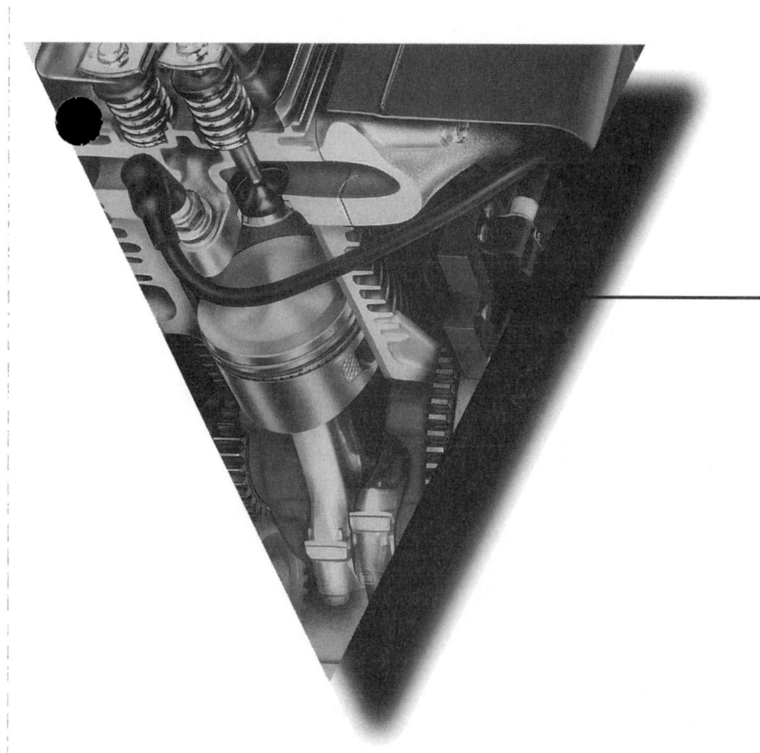

Ignition Systems

Name________________________________

Date ____________________ Period ___________

Instructor______________________________

After studying this chapter, you will be able to:

- ▼ List the primary purposes of the ignition system.
- ▼ Identify the components in a typical magneto system and describe the function of each part.
- ▼ Describe small engine ignition advance systems.
- ▼ List the advantages of a solid state ignition system.
- ▼ Identify the three general classifications of magneto ignition systems and explain the operation of each.
- ▼ Describe the operation of a battery ignition system.

Instructions: After studying Chapter 9 of the text, complete the following questions and problems.

1. The primary purpose of the ignition system of a small gasoline engine is to provide sufficient electrical voltage to discharge _____.
   a. gasoline
   b. air
   c. a spark between the electrodes of the spark plug
   d. a spark to create flashover

   1. ____________________________

2. The ignition system must be capable of producing as much as _____ volts to force the electrical current across the plug gap.

   2. ____________________________

3. A single cylinder, four-cycle engine running at 3000 rpm requires _____ ignition sparks per minute or _____ sparks per second.

   3. ____________________________
   ____

4. List the three types of magnetos in use on small gas engines.

____

____

____

5. Identify the basic parts of the magneto ignition system shown below.

5. A. ______________________________
B. ______________________________
C. ______________________________
D. ______________________________
E. ______________________________
F. ______________________________
G. ______________________________
H. ______________________________

6. Electrons travel in _____ around the center of an atom. 6. ______________________________

7. Electrons have _____ electrical charges, and protons have _____ electrical charges. 7. ______________________________
____

8. Neutrons and protons make up the _____ of an atom. 8. ______________________________

9. In any atom, the electrons are equal in number to the ______. 9. ______________________________

10. Explain why electrons do not collide with one another. ______________________________

____

____

11. Electrons tend to stay in orbits due to their attraction by _____. 11. ______________________________

12. If an electron can transfer from atom to atom easily, the material is said to be a good electrical _____. 12. ______________________________

13. List three ways in which an electrical potential is produced and give an example of each one.

____

____

____

Name ______________________________

14. Identify the positive and negative battery terminals indicated on the illustration below.

14. A. ______________________

B. ______________________

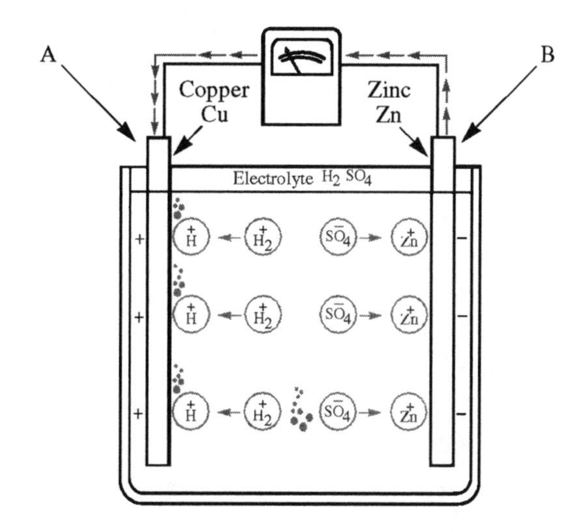

15. Name the electrical units described below.
    A. Force that causes electrons to flow
    B. Rate of electron flow
    C. Resistance to electron flow

15. A. ______________________

B. ______________________

C. ______________________

16. Explain why high voltage is required in an ignition system. ______________________

____

____

17. According to Ohm's law, if the voltage is 110, and the resistance is 11 ohms, the current would be _____ amperes.

17. ______________________

18. According to Ohm's law, if the amperage in a circuit is 5 and the voltage is 14, the resistance is _____ ohms.

18. ______________________

19. According to Ohm's law, if the amperage is 3 and the resistance is 30, the voltage is _____ volts.

19. ______________________

20. Magnetic materials have _____ that are aligned so their north poles are all in one direction and south poles are in the opposite direction.

20. ______________________

21. In magnets, opposite poles _____ each other and like poles _____ each other.

21. ______________________

____

22. Electricity can be produced by passing a wire through a(n) _____ field.

22. ______________________

23. When electricity flows through a coil wire, a(n) _____ _____ is developed.

23. ______________________

24. Identify the parts of the ignition coil shown below.

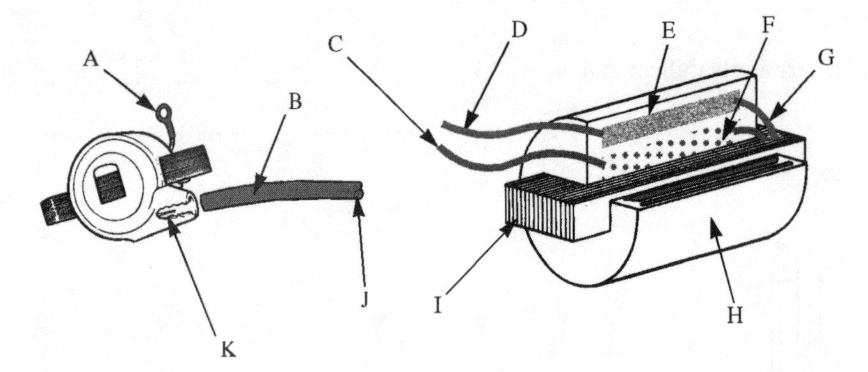

24. A. ____
B. ____
C. ____
D. ____
E. ____
F. ____
G. ____
H. ____
I. ____
J. ____
K. ____

25. In an ignition coil, the primary windings are _____.
    a. light gage with many turns
    b. heavy gage with few turns
    c. light gage with few turns
    d. heavy gage with many turns

25. ____

26. The windings connected directly to the high tension spark plug lead are the _____ windings.
    a. secondary
    b. primary

26. ____

27. A magnetic field is created around the iron core when current is passed through the _____ windings.

27. ____

28. High secondary voltage is created when the current in the primary coil is _____ and the magnetic field _____.

28. ____
____

29. Identify the spark plug parts indicated below.

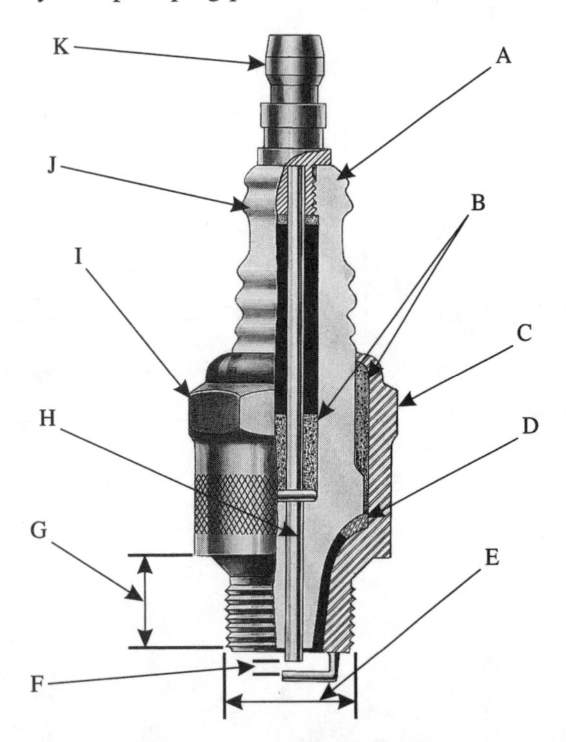

29. A. ____
B. ____
C. ____
D. ____
E. ____
F. ____
G. ____
H. ____
I. ____
J. ____
K. ____

Name ______________________________

30. List three characteristics the ceramic spark plug insulator must have.

____

____

____

31. Ribs on the ceramic spark plug insulator are there to prevent _____. 31. ______________________________

32. Identify which of the following plugs would be considered *hot* and which would be considered *cold*. 32. A. ____________ B. ____________ C. ____________ D. ____________

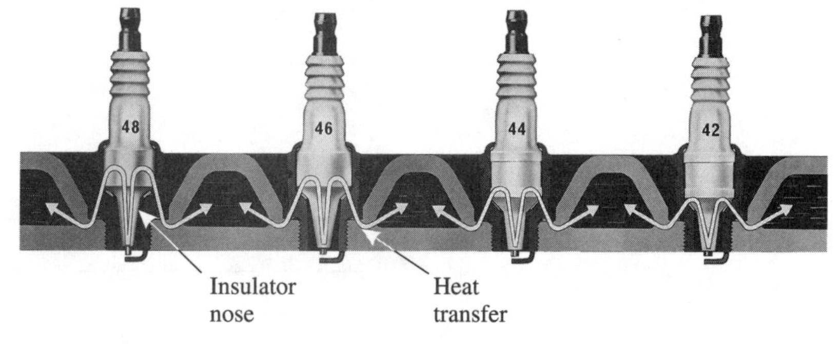

A B C D

33. In figuring spark plug heat range, the length of the _____ _____ determines how far and how well the heat travels. 33. ______________________________

34. The hottest part of the spark plug is the _____ of the insulator. 34. ______________________________

35. Experiments show that preigniton is likely to occur if combustion chamber temperature exceeds _____ in a four-cycle engine. 35. ______________________________

36. If the insulator tip temperature is below 700°F (371°C), plug _____ or _____ is likely to occur. 36. ______________________________

____

37. Identify the parts of the breaker point assembly shown below. 37. A. ____________ B. ____________ C. ____________ D. ____________ E. ____________ F. ____________ G. ____________ H. ____________ I. ____________ J. ____________ K. ____________

K
A
J
B
C
I
D
E
F
H
G

38. The breaker point contacts are made of _____.
39. The breaker point system is actually an electrical _____.
40. The high voltage to spark the spark plug is induced in the secondary windings only when the breaker points _____.
41. The main purpose of the condenser is to prevent _____ across the breaker point gap as the points open.
42. A condenser must be selected that has the correct _____ to absorb the amount of energy required to produce an arc.
43. A condenser absorbs current at the exact time the breaker points _____.
44. Identify the parts indicated on the condenser illustrated below.

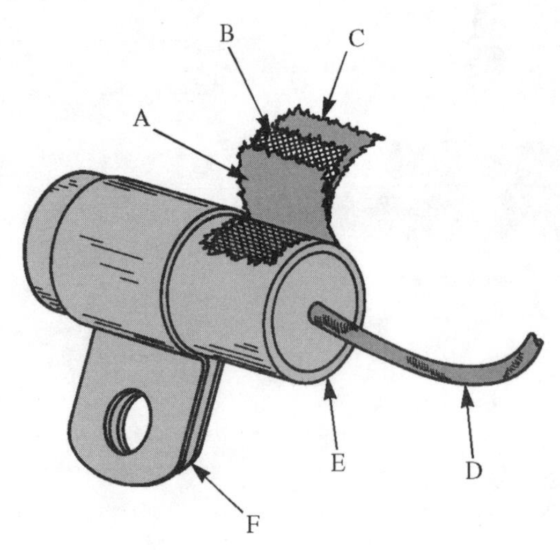

38. ____________
39. ____________
40. ____________
41. ____________
42. ____________
43. ____________
44. A. ____________
B. ____________
C. ____________
D. ____________
E. ____________
F. ____________

45. Identify the major components of the typical flywheel magneto ignition system shown below.

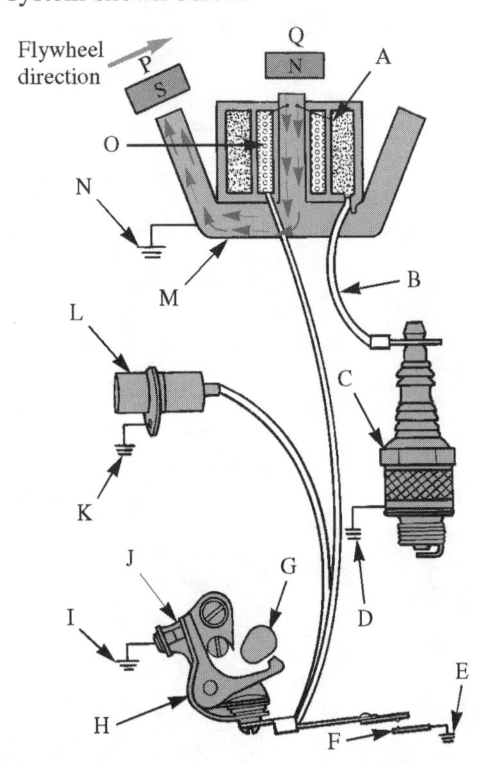

45. A. ____________
B. ____________
C. ____________
D. ____________
E. ____________
F. ____________
G. ____________
H. ____________
I. ____________
J. ____________
K. ____________
L. ____________
M. ____________
N. ____________
O. ____________
P. ____________
Q. ____________

Name ____

46. The spacing between the flywheel magnets and the core ends is called the _____ _____. 46. ____________________________

47. The breaker points are opened by the _____ and closed by the breaker point spring. 47. ____________________________

48. Two methods commonly used to stop the engine are to ground the breaker points with a stop switch, or to ground the _____ _____ wire. 48. ____________________________

49. When starting an engine with an advance system, the spark timing should be _____. 49. ____________________________

50. High speed operations require the spark timing to be automatically _____. 50. ____________________________

51. Dwell is the time the breaker points stay _____ during one revolution of the cam. 51. ____________________________

52. A large breaker point gap will produce a(n) _____ dwell. 52. ____________________________

53. Changing the point gap setting can also change spark _____. 53. ____________________________

54. Explain why no mechanical adjustments are necessary in a solid state ignition system.____________________

____

____

55. Describe how a CDI module can be tested to see if it is producing a spark. ____________________________

____

____

____

56. The _____ _____ is the most vulnerable part of the solid state ignition system. 56. ____________________________

57. List 10 advantages of solid state ignition systems.

____

____

____

____

____

____

____

____

____

____

58. A(n) _____ _____ ignition system is a flywheel magneto inductive system that employs mechanical breaker contacts to time or trigger the system. 58. ____________________________

59. A(n) _____ _____ ignition system is an inductive system that does not use mechanical breaker contacts. It utilizes semiconductors for switching purposes. 59. ______________________

60. A(n) _____ _____ ignition system is a solid state system which stores its primary energy in a capacitor and uses semiconductors for timing or triggering the system. 60. ______________________

61. The basic difference between a magneto and a battery ignition system is that the _____ current is supplied by a(n) _____ - _____ battery. 61. ______________________
____

62. The auto-transformer coil used on some small engines increases low voltage _____ current to the high voltage required to bridge the spark plug gap. 62. ______________________

63. The positive terminal must be connected to the _____ side of the battery. 63. ______________________

64. The lead-acid battery has cell plates made of _____, and a(n) _____ acid and water solution serves as the electrolyte. 64. ______________________
____

65. The ampere-hour rating (capacity) of a battery is directly related to the number of _____ per _____. 65. ______________________
____

66. A chemical reaction in the battery causes the negative plates to _____ (lose, gain) electrons and each positive plate to _____ (lose, gain) electrons producing an electrical potential. 66. ______________________
____

67. When a battery _____ without replacement of energy, the sulfuric acid is chemically withdrawn from the electrolyte, specific gravity goes down, and lead sulfite deposits accumulate on the plates. 67. ______________________

68. The ignition (spark) should begin at _____. 68. ______________________
   a. exactly TDC
   b. a predetermined point before TDC
   c. 25° to 35° after TDC
   d. 7° after TDC

69. In CDI ignitions systems, the _____ is triggered to create a path to ground through the coil. 69. ______________________
   a. exciter coil
   b. capacitor
   c. secondary circuit
   d. SCR

70. The output voltage required to create a spark is controlled by _____. 70. ______________________
   a. resistance in the coil
   b. pressure of combustion and spark plug gap
   c. spark plug heat range
   d. condenser capacitance

Name ______________________________

71. The engine stop switch in a magneto ignition system _____ the primary circuit. In a battery ignition system the stop switch _____ primary circuit.
    a. opens, shorts
    b. shorts, opens

71. ______________________

72. A diode in a TCI ignition system allows passage of dc current in _____ direction(s).

72. ______________________

• Research and write complete answers to the following questions.

73. Explain how the traditional MBI (conventional) magneto ignition system works. Describe the function of each of the components.______________________________

74. Describe the importance of the spark plug gap setting and heat range. What controls or determines the heat range of a spark plug? ______________________________

75. Describe proper care of a lead-acid battery including testing and charging procedures. Include safe handling and emergency procedures. ______________________________

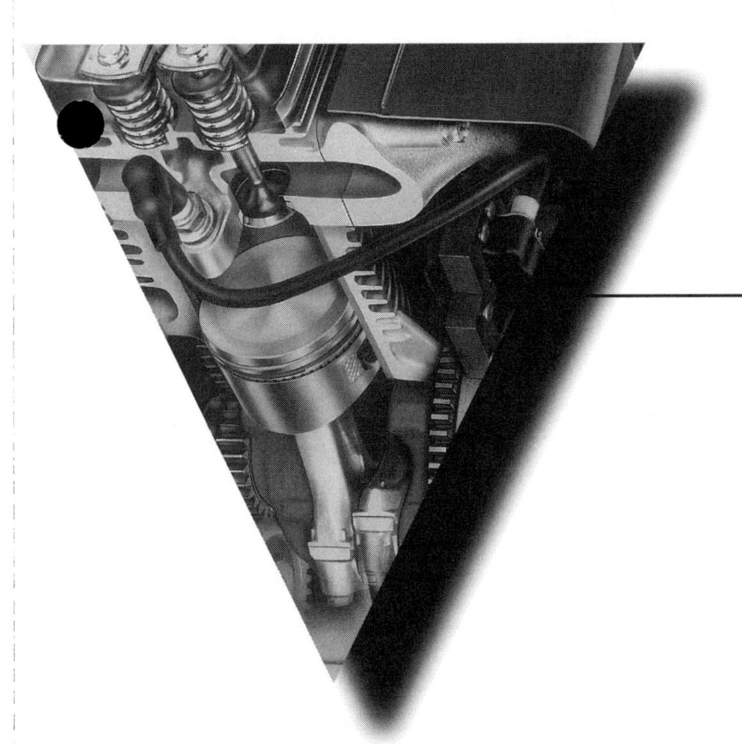

Lubrication Systems

Name_______________________________

Date ____________________ Period __________

Instructor___________________________

After studying this chapter, you will be able to:

- ▼ Define friction and explain how it affects the internal engine components.
- ▼ List the functions of lubricating oil.
- ▼ Differentiate between the lubrication systems in two-cycle engines and four-cycle engines.
- ▼ Explain the operation of injection pumps, barrel pumps, and positive displacement pumps.
- ▼ Explain the function of oil filter systems and differentiate between the three main types.

Instructions: After studying Chapter 10 in the text, complete the following questions and problems.

1. _____ is the process of reducing friction between sliding surfaces by introducing a slippery or smooth substance between them. 1. ____________________
2. _____ is the resistance to movement when one dry surface moves against another. 2. ____________________
3. If lubrication is inadequate or non-existent in an engine, parts can _____, thus stopping the engine and causing great damage. 3. ____________________
4. When lubricated parts are in motion, _____ molecules roll over one another like microscopic ball bearings. 4. ____________________
5. The bearing surface in the precision bearing insert is made of a metal called _____ because it has good anti-friction qualities. 5. ____________________
6. To keep the bearing insert from rotating in the connecting rod, projections called _____ _____ are used. 6. ____________________

For questions 7 through 12, the major parts of a small gasoline engine that require a coating of lubrication are given. Name the part in contact. (See the following example.)

Example: Piston and Cylinder

7. Piston rings and _____ 7. ____________________
8. Piston pin and _____ 8. ____________________
9. Connecting rod and _____ 9. ____________________
10. Valve stem and _____ 10. ____________________
11. Crankshaft and _____ 11. ____________________
12. Valve tappets and _____ 12. ____________________
13. List eight important functions that oil performs in an engine.

____
____
____
____
____
____
____
____

14. Oil is expected to maintain a complete, unbroken film between mating parts. Lubrication engineers call this full-film or _____ lubrication. 14. ____________________
15. When oil cannot maintain a full-film condition and intermittent metal-to-metal contact is made, it is referred to as _____ lubrication. 15. ____________________
16. For each gallon of fuel burned, more than _____ _____ of water is formed. 16. ____________________
17. A good engine oil has the ability to _____ the effects of the corrosive by-products of combustion. 17. ____________________
18. _____ are added to mineral oils to prevent varnish deposits from forming on critical engine parts. 18. ____________________
19. Like air, oil helps keep engine parts _____. 19. ____________________
20. Proper oil helps provide a good _____ between the piston rings and the cylinder wall. 20. ____________________
21. The recommended oil for a specific engine may be found on the engine's _____ or on a label attached to the engine. Another source for this information is the _____ _____. 21. ____________________ ____________________
22. Name the two ratings given for specifications of engine oils.

____
____

Name ______________________________

23. Viscosity refers to the resistance of a liquid to flow. In general, would a low or high viscosity oil be used in cold temperature operation? 23. ______________

24. What does the W represent in a multi-viscosity grade oil such as SAE 5 W-20? 24. ______________

25. The top portion of the API engine oil service classification symbol specifies the oil's _____ classification. 25. ______________

26. Why are special oils recommended for use in two-cycle engines?______________

____

____

27. Small four-cycle gasoline engines generally use some type of _____ system to lubricate internal mechanical surfaces. 27. ______________

28. In engines with a splash lubrication system, oil _____ _____ prevents oil burning problems. 28. ______________

29. Oil pumps are used to force oil under pressure through channels to various engine parts. Name three types of oil pumps discussed in the text.

____

____

____

30. Positive displacement pumps require a(n) _____ _____ valve in case there is a restriction to normal oil flow in the system. 30. ______________

31. What is the purpose of an oil filter? ______________

____

32. List the three basic types of oil filter systems.

____

____

____

- Research and write complete answers to the following questions.

33. Explain the best procedure for changing the oil in a lawn mower engine so as to remove the maximum contamination.

____

____

____

____

____

____

____

34. Describe the proper method of mixing oil and fuel for use in a two-cycle engine. How should an oil-fuel mixture be treated if it is not going to be used for a long period? ______________________________

35. Describe the possible mechanical effects of using oil that is contaminated with dirt. Include visual indications on parts that dirty oil has been used. Where does the dirt come from? ______________________________

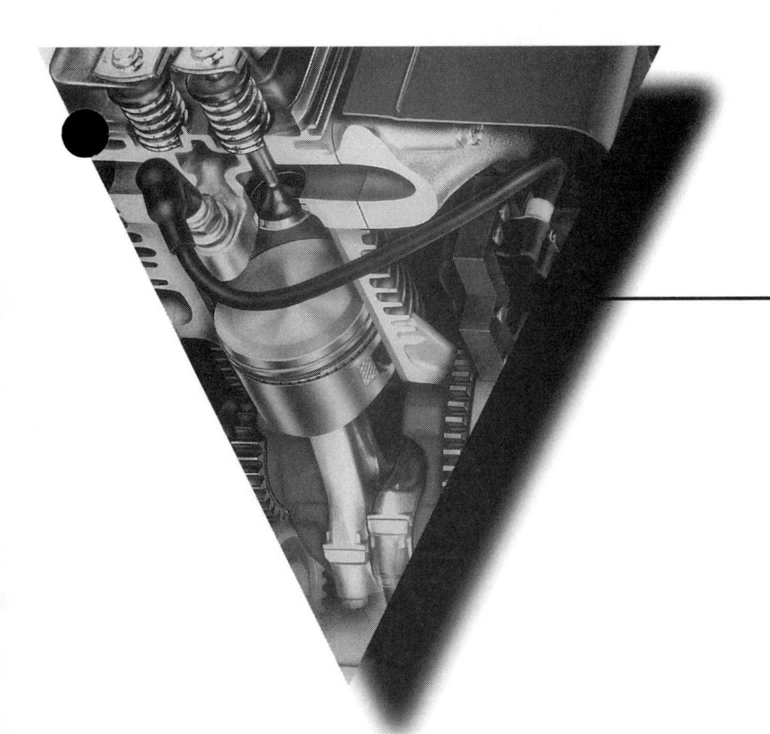

CHAPTER 11

Cooling Systems

Name________________________________

Date ____________________ Period ____________

Instructor____________________________

After studying this chapter, you will be able to:

- ▼ Explain how air cooling, exhaust cooling, and water cooling work to lower engine operating temperatures.
- ▼ Define the basic function of a water pump and give examples of several common types.
- ▼ Describe the basic operation of outboard water circulation systems.
- ▼ Explain the function of a thermostat and a radiator.

Instructions: After studying Chapter 11 in the text, complete the following questions and problems.

1. The average temperature of burned gases in the combustion chamber of an air-cooled engine is _____. 1. ____________________
2. The air cooling system removes about _____ of the heat. 2. ____________________
3. Cylinders on air-cooled engines are covered with cooling _____ to increase the surface area and cooling efficiency. 3. ____________________
4. Air is forced around the cylinders by the _____. 4. ____________________
5. The direction of airflow over the engine is controlled by a cover called the _____. 5. ____________________
6. Heat traveling through a solid material is called _____. 6. ____________________
7. Heat moved by air is called _____. 7. ____________________
8. Explain why cylinders, and engines in general, should be kept clean.____________________

____

____

9. How might an engine overheat due to exhaust gases? ______________________________

____

____

10. Exhaust gasses carry away about _____ of the heat from the engine. 10. ______________
    a. one-half
    b. one-third
    c. one-fourth
    d. three-fourths

11. Excessive heat in an engine increases _____ and maintenance costs. 11. ______________

12. Dirt, grass clippings, leaves, straw, or other material lodged between the cooling fins will tend to _____ the cylinder and cause hot spots and engine overheating. 12. ______________

13. Water is _____ times more effective for cooling than air. 13. ______________

14. Give three reasons why water is a good cooling medium for engines.

____

____

____

15. Cylinders of water-cooled engines are surrounded by a(n) _____ _____. 15. ______________

16. Identify the parts of the water-cooled engine illustrated below. 16. A. ______________

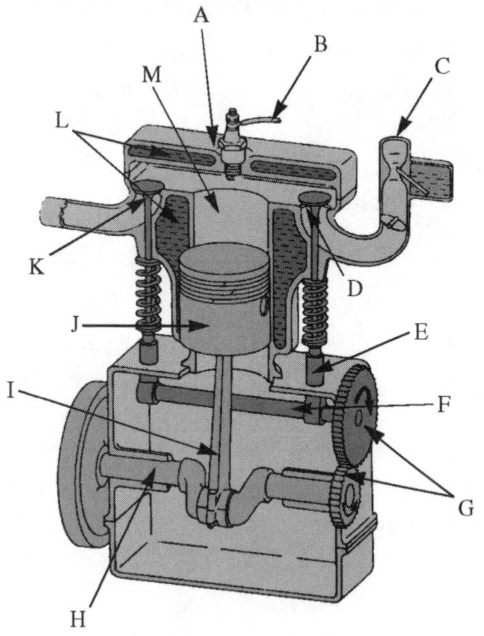

B. ______________

C. ______________

D. ______________

E. ______________

F. ______________

G. ______________

H. ______________

I. ______________

J. ______________

K. ______________

L. ______________

M. ______________

Name ________________________________

17. In cold temperatures, _____ is added to the water in the proper amounts to prevent freezing. 17. ____________________

18. The _____ _____ in the revolving cam type water pump acts to prevent excessive water pressure during high speed operation. 18. ____________________

19. Plunger pumps for water cooling use _____ _____ valves for the inlet and outlet of the pump. 19. ____________________

20. The impeller in the vari-volume water pump is made of _____ _____. 20. ____________________

21. A thermostat will _____ when cooling water temperature reaches proper engine operating temperature. 21. ____________________

22. _____ are reservoirs for water made of many thin copper or aluminum tubes. 22. ____________________

23. The fine balance of cooling maintained by the radiator and _____ assures that the engine will not overheat under loads in the hot summer or run too cold in the winter. 23. ____________________

24. Besides water, _____ is another liquid found in all engines that also acts as a coolant. 24. ____________________

25. If the air/fuel mixture is too lean, the engine will run _____. 25. ____________________
    a. hotter
    b. cooler

26. In a radiator cooling system, the hot water enters the radiator at the _____. 26. ____________________
    a. top
    b. bottom
    c. center

27. When engine temperature is below normal, the water _____ the radiator and returns to the _____. 27. ____________________
    ____

• Research and write complete answers to the following questions.

28. Make a sequential list of procedures that would check out the entire cooling system of an air-cooled engine.

____

____

____

____

29. Explain how oil contributes to cooling each part of an engine.

____

____

____

____

30. Describe how a thermostatically controlled cooling system for outboard engines works. Begin at the cold water intake. Refer to the illustration below.

____

____

____

____

____

____

____

____

____

____

____

____

____

____

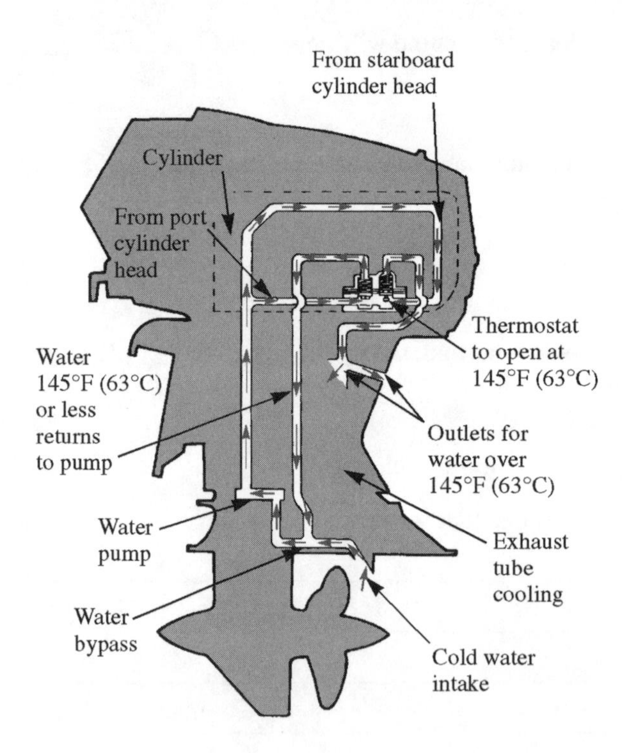

Preventive Maintenance and Troubleshooting

Name____________________

Date ______________ Period ________

Instructor____________________

After studying this chapter, you will be able to:

- ▼ Keep engines clean.
- ▼ Change the oil in a four-cycle engine.
- ▼ Mix fuel and oil correctly for a two-cycle engine.
- ▼ Perform preventive maintenance on various engine systems, including the crankcase breather, air cleaner, and muffler.
- ▼ Prepare a water cooling system for storage.
- ▼ Describe systematic troubleshooting.
- ▼ Use manufacturer's service manuals to determine engine specifications and explain why this information is necessary when servicing a small engine.

Instructions: After studying Chapter 12 in the text, complete the following questions and problems.

1. A simple preventive maintenance procedure that can help prevent overheating is _____ the external parts of the engine. 1. ____________

2. If an engine overheats, parts will _____. 2. ____________
   a. distort
   b. possibly seize
   c. expand
   d. All of the above.

3. Describe three safety rules for using compressed air when cleaning an engine, or parts. ____________

____

____

____

4. Name several safe, effective methods for cleaning the external parts of an engine. ______________________
____
____
____
____

5. All oil dipsticks will have _____ and _____ marks. 5. ______________________
____

6. Overfilling a crankcase with oil can cause the engine to ______________________
____.

7. Engines that do not have a dipstick have a filler plug. The oil should be filled to the ______________________
____.

8. List the contaminants that can be found in used engine oil.
____
____
____
____

9. To remove most contaminants from oil when draining, it is best to _____. 9. ______________________
   a. mix kerosene with the oil before draining
   b. drain the oil cold so the contaminants do not settle to the bottom of the crankcase
   c. run the engine to warm the oil so it will flow more thoroughly
   d. shake the engine to suspend all the dirt in the oil before draining

10. When changing or adding oil to an engine, the manufacturer's recommended _____ should be used. 10. ______________________
   a. viscosity and grade
   b. type
   c. quantity
   d. All of the above.

11. Why should fuel containers and fuel tanks be kept full if they are stored where temperatures may vary frequently? ______________________
____
____

12. List the three types of air cleaners used on small gas engines.
____
____
____

Name ________________________________

13. Identify the parts of the crankcase breather illustrated below.

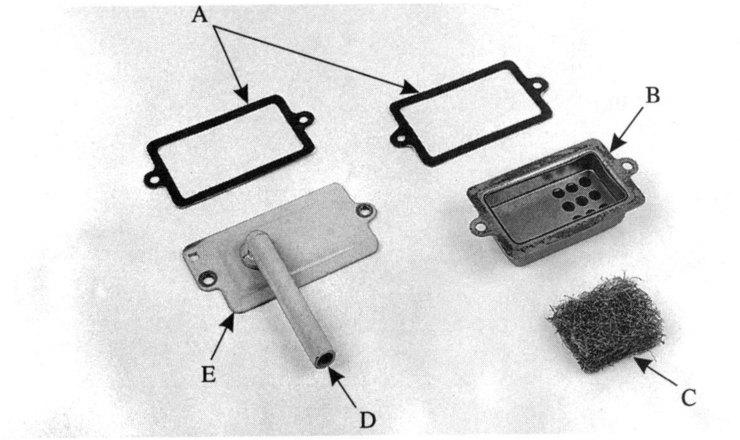

A
B
E
D
C

13. A________________________
B. ________________________
C. ________________________
D. ________________________
E. ________________________

14. The crankcase breather allows air flow _____.
   a. outward only
   b. inward only
   c. both inward and outward

14. ________________________

15. A muffler is designed to _____.
   a. reduce noise
   b. remove condensation
   c. allow gasses to escape
   d. Both a and c.

15. ________________________

16. When a muffler becomes clogged with carbon soot, the result can be ________________________

____.

17. _____ should *never* be used to clean a muffler.

17. ________________________

18. Water-cooled engines can have a(n) _____ added to the cooling system.

18. ________________________

19. For efficient radiator heat transfer, the _____ and _____ must be kept clean.

19. ________________________

____

20. When cleaning debris from the outside of a radiator, low pressure air or water can be used. It should be directed _____.
   a. in the same direction the air flows
   b. opposite the direction the air flows
   c. It makes no difference.

20. ________________________

21. Radiators and engine blocks can be cleaned by _____ flushing the system with pressurized water.

21. ________________________

22. When refilling a radiator for use in moderately warm temperatures, the water should be mixed _____ with an Ethylene Glycol antifreeze.
   a. one-third and two-thirds
   b. one-half and one-half
   c. one-quarter and three-quarters
   d. one-eighth and seven-eighths

22. ________________________

23. Outboard engines used in saltwater should be flushed with _____ _____ after use. 23. ____________

24. If an outboard engine cannot be removed from the water immediately after operation, it should be _____ so the _____ is out of the water and rinsed with fresh water. 24. ____________ ____________

25. When storing water-cooled engines with radiators in the winter, _____ with a rust inhibitor should be added to the water. 25. ____________

26. When storing outboard engines during winter, all _____ should be removed from the gearcase and driveshaft housing. 26. ____________

27. A(n) _____ approach should be taken when troubleshooting a small gas engine. 27. ____________

28. List the five fundamental operating requirements necessary for proper engine operation.

____

____

____

____

____

29. What are the two basic principles to follow when attempting to locate small engine problems? ____________

____

____

30. You can often get valuable information relating to the condition of an engine from the _____. 30. ____________

31. If an engine stalls after 30–45 minutes of operation but will start again immediately, the problem is probably in the _____ _____. 31. ____________

32. By spinning an engine, you can determine whether there is adequate _____ and _____. 32. ____________ ____________

33. If an engine stalls and will not start again until after it cools down, the problem may be _____ _____ or sticking valves. 33. ____________

34. Before working on an engine, always consult the _____ _____ for appropriate service procedures. 34. ____________

35. A(n) _____ _____ lists common engine malfunctions, possible causes, and suggested remedies. 35. ____________

36. What does it mean when tolerance specifications show two values? ____________

____

____

37. A stroboscope is a device for measuring engine _____. 37. ____________

38. If an engine lacks power, a compression test may be required to determine the _____ of the piston, cylinder, and valves. 38. ____________

Name ________________________________

39. List the six steps that should be followed when performing a compression test.

____

____

____

____

____

____

40. If an engine has a(n) _____ _____ system, it may have to be cranked in reverse to obtain an accurate reading during a compression test. 40. ____________________

41. An engine that produces less compression than the manufacturer's recommendations, usually has one or more problems. List at least five of the possible problems.

____

____

____

____

____

____

____

____

42. A(n) _____ _____ test can identify a specific worn or damaged component without taking the engine apart. 42. ____________________

43. Troubleshooting charts found in service manuals list _____. 43. ____________________
    a. symptoms
    b. causes
    c. remedies
    d. All of the above.

44. Refer to text Figure 12-16, Engine Troubleshooting Chart. If an engine misses under load and you find a faulty condenser, you should ____

____.

45. If an engine vibrates excessively and you find the engine not securely mounted, you should ____________

____.

46. If you discover that an engine shows abrasives on a worn choke and throttle plate and the choke and throttle shafts are loose, what is the probable cause? Refer to text Appendix under Engine Failure Analysis.

____

47. What are three effects of overspeeding an engine? Refer to text Appendix under Engine Failure Analysis.

____

____

____

48. A(n) _____ and _____ chart generally contains information on spark plug gap, breaker point gap, and ignition timing.
48. ______________________________
____

49. Many bolts and nuts must be tightened to exact _____ specifications.
49. ______________________________

50. Overtightening a bolt may result in a(n) _____ bolt or _____ threads.
50. ______________________________
____

51. Overtightening bolts and nuts can cause excessive stresses within parts and lead to _____ or part _____.
51. ______________________________
____

52. When several bolts are required to fasten mating parts together, they should be tightened in proper _____ to prevent part distortion and/or fluid leaks.
52. ______________________________

53. How many inch pounds of torque should be applied to an SAE 5 bolt with a 5/16 inch diameter shank? Refer to Torque Chart in text Appendix.
a. 116 inch pounds
b. 224 inch pounds
c. 168 inch pounds
d. Inch pounds cannot be used.
53. ______________________________

54. How many Newton-meters of torque would be equal to 25 foot pounds? Refer to Torque Chart in text Appendix.
54. ______________________________

55. If a plated 3/8 inch diameter bolt of SAE 2 grade is used, what should the foot pounds of torque be? Refer to Torque Chart in text Appendix.
55. ______________________________

• Research and write complete answers to the following questions.

56. Explain the order in which you would handle a troubleshooting problem for a lawn mower that will not start. Refer to text Figure 12-16, Engine Troubleshooting Chart. ______________________________

____

____

____

____

____

57. Describe the proper procedure for carrying out a differential compression test on a two-cylinder snowmobile engine.

____

____

____

____

____

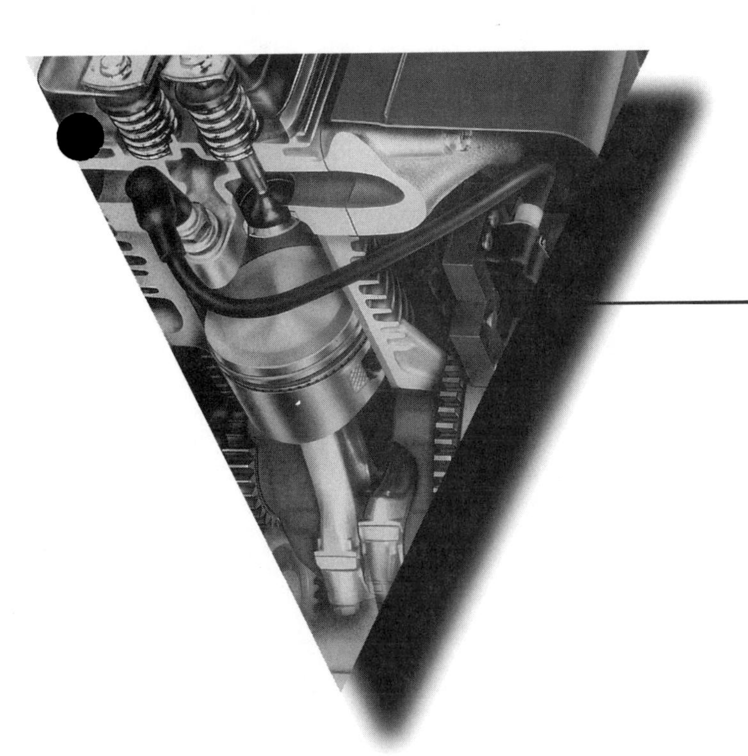

Fuel System Service

Name____________________________________

Date ____________________ Period ____________

Instructor__________________________________

After studying this chapter, you will be able to:

- ▼ Test a fuel pump for proper operation.
- ▼ Summarize basic carburetor adjustments.
- ▼ Test two-cycle engine reeds for leakage.
- ▼ Explain basic procedures for inspecting, overhauling, and adjusting diaphragm and float-type carburetors.
- ▼ Troubleshoot float-type and diaphragm-type carburetors.

Instructions: After studying Chapter 13 in the text, complete the following questions and problems.

1. Identify the parts of the sediment bowl shown in the figure below.

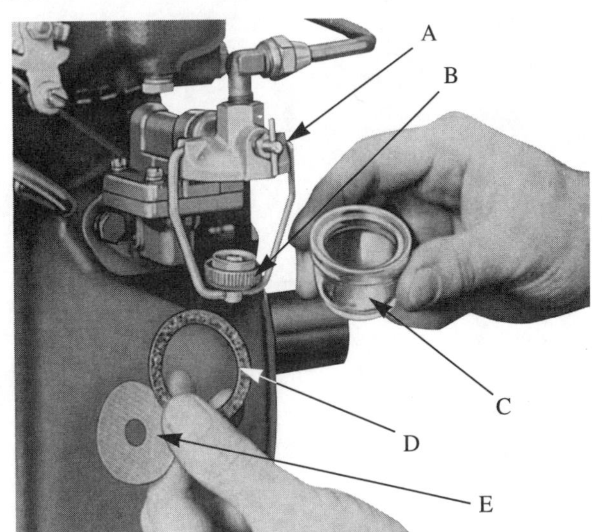

1. A. ________________________
   B. ________________________
   C. ________________________
   D. ________________________
   E. ________________________

2. If an engine has a sediment bowl on the fuel strainer and water is present in the fuel, the water will _____.
   a. float on top of the fuel
   b. not be visible
   c. settle to the bottom of the bowl
   d. escape from the sediment bowl

   2. ______________________

3. If an engine is equipped with a fuel pump and fuel is not being delivered to the carburetor, check to see that _____.
   a. there is fuel in the gas tank
   b. the fittings connecting the fuel line to the tank and pump are tight
   c. the pump filter is clean and the gasket on the filter bowl is in good condition
   d. the pump is actually working
   e. All of the above.

   3. ______________________

4. The two needle valve adjustments found on most carburetors are the _____ speed adjustment and the _____ mixture adjustment.

   4. ______________________
   ____

5. Because there are many different designs, you should always follow the _____ _____ when assembling a carburetor.

   5. ______________________

6. If the float is set too high in a float-type carburetor, the engine will run _____.

   6. ______________________

7. Before making fine adjustments to a carburetor, the engine should be _____ _____.

   7. ______________________

8. List four steps for adjusting the high speed carburetor needle.

____

____

____

____

9. List three steps for adjusting the idle mixture needle.

____

____

____

10. List three effects of leaking two-cycle engine reeds.

____

____

____

11. A carburetor overhaul generally consists of _____, _____, and replacing parts.

   11. ______________________
   ____

12. A carburetor overhaul can be made much easier by obtaining an appropriate carburetor overhaul _____.

   12. ______________________

Name ______________________________

13. List the nine typical procedures that should be followed when removing a carburetor.

____

____

____

____

____

____

____

____

____

14. When disassembling a carburetor, all _____ parts should be removed. 14. _______________

15. _____ carburetor parts should never be placed in cleaning solvents. 15. _______________

16. To expose carburetor passages, welch plugs should be removed with a small, sharp _____. 16. _______________

17. When replacing welch plugs, they should be inserted with the curved side _____ and tapped into place with a(n) _____. 17. _______________

____

18. List the eight rules that should be observed when making float-type carburetor repairs.

____

____

____

____

____

____

____

____

19. Why should the throttle plate screws and the choke plate screws be replaced with new ones when assembling a carburetor? _______________________________

____

____

20. After all parts are clean and dry, they should be inspected for _____ and _____. 20. _______________

____

21. The tips of the idle mixture and high speed needles should be _____ and _____. 21. _______________

____

22. Many choke and throttle plates have _____ _____ on them so that they can be installed in the proper position. 22. ______________

23. The choke shaft, throttle shaft, and bearing holes should be examined for _____. 23. ______________

24. It is important to inspect hollow, brass-type floats for _____ and _____. 24. ______________ ______________

25. When installing a new inlet needle seat, the smooth side of the seat should be installed _____ the inlet needle. 25. ______________
    a. toward
    b. away from

26. List the symptoms of a worn throttle and/or choke shaft. Refer to text Figure 13-23, Troubleshooting Float-Type Carburetors. ______________

27. Why should low-pressure compressed air be used instead of a rag or paper towel to dry carburetor parts?

____

28. If the throttle and/or choke shafts are loose (worn holes or shafts), the engine will run _____. 28. ______________
    a. rich
    b. lean
    c. erratic and lean
    d. erratic and rich

29. Identify the parts of the float-type carburetor shown below.

A
B
C
D
E
F

29. A. ______________
B. ______________
C. ______________
D. ______________
E. ______________
F. ______________

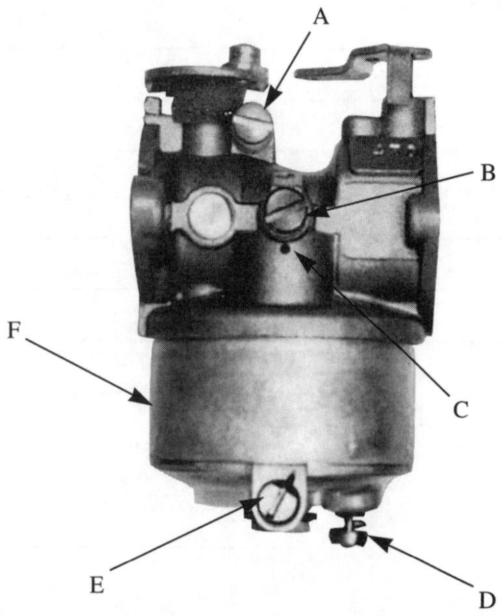

Name ____

30. Identify the float parts shown below.

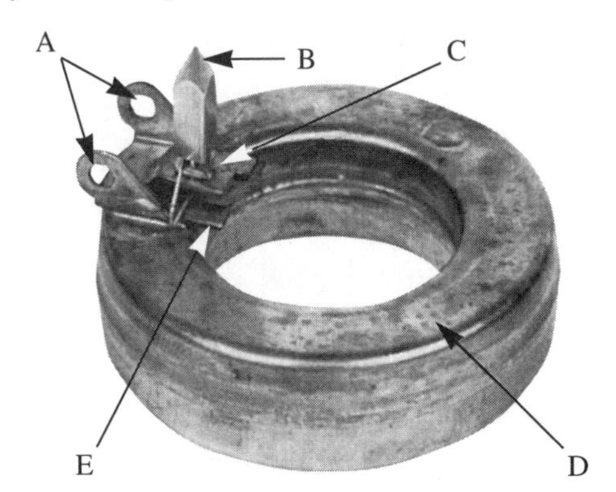

30. A. ______________________
    B. ______________________
    C. ______________________
    D. ______________________
    E. ______________________

31. The plunger-type primer bulb, when pressed, forces fuel through the main _____ _____ and into the carburetor throat.

31. ______________________

32. When the primer bulb is pressed, it forces air into the _____ _____ on float-type carburetors.

32. ______________________

33. If the float-type carburetor on an engine floods and leaks fuel, the problem may be _____. Refer to text Figure 13-23, Troubleshooting Float-Type Carburetors.
    a. improper float height
    b. a restricted atmospheric vent
    c. a plugged atmospheric vent
    d. All of the above.

33. ______________________

34. A float that is set low will cause the engine to run _____.
    a. lean
    b. rich
    c. better

34. ______________________

35. When servicing a diaphragm carburetor, the diaphragm should be checked for defects that can cause _____.

35. ______________________

36. The diaphragm needle valve must fit the seat properly, so that it _____ when it is closed.

36. ______________________

37. Identify the parts of the diaphragm carburetor repair kit shown below.

37. A. ______________________
    B. ______________________
    C. ______________________
    D. ______________________
    E. ______________________
    F. ______________________
    G. ______________________
    H. ______________________

38. List four symptoms for leaky diaphragm carburetor gaskets. Refer to text Figure 13-33, Troubleshooting Diaphragm Carburetors.

____

____

____

____

39. If a diaphragm-type carburetor floods and/or leaks the problem may be a cracked or brittle _____. Refer to text Figure 13-33, Troubleshooting Diaphragm Carburetors.

39. _______________

40. The two types of governors used on small gas engines are _____-_____ and _____ _____.

40. _______________

____

41. Air or centrifugal force is used to _____ spring pressure in small engine governors.

41. _______________

• Research and write complete answers to the following questions.

42. Describe the correct procedure for adjusting a carburetor that has been overhauled and reinstalled on an engine.

____

____

____

____

____

____

43. After studying Chapter 13, describe what you think is the best procedure for carburetor disassembly, cleaning, inspection, and reassembly. _______________

____

____

____

____

44. Describe each of the things you should examine when inspecting a float-type carburetor during disassembly.

____

____

____

____

____

45. Describe each of the things you should examine when inspecting a diaphragm-type carburetor during disassembly.

____

____

____

____

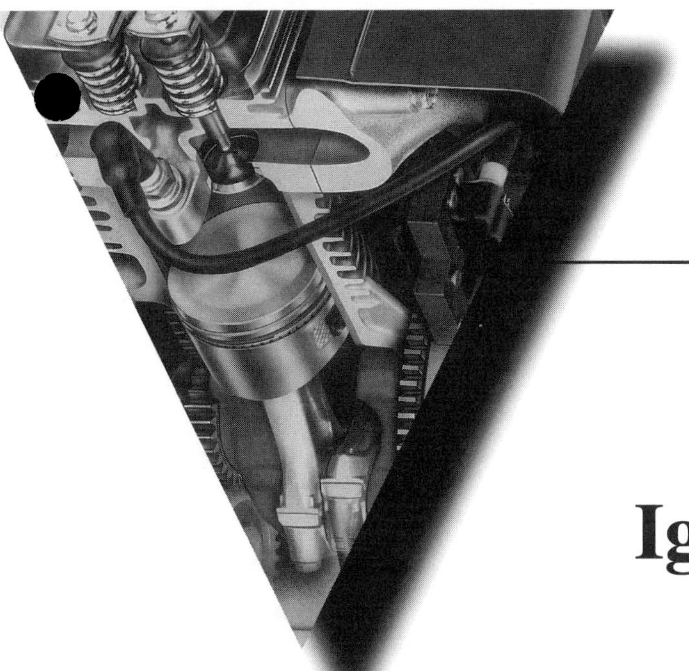

Ignition System Service

Name______________________________________

Date _____________________ Period ____________

Instructor____________________________________

After studying this chapter, you will be able to:

- ▼ Examine spark plug deposits for signs of abnormal combustion.
- ▼ Clean, gap, and install spark plugs correctly.
- ▼ Explain the basic inspections and tests used to verify proper ignition system operation.
- ▼ Adjust breaker points, piston height, and ignition spark timing.
- ▼ Explain basic tests for breaker point and solid state ignition systems.
- ▼ Explain typical service procedures for battery ignition systems.

Instructions: After studying Chapter 14 in the text, complete the following questions and problems.

1. Ignition system service involves the _____.
   a. coil windings
   b. spark plugs
   c. ignition ground
   d. All of the above.

   1. ________________________

2. The magneto system will provide only the amount of _____ needed to jump the spark plug _____.

   2. ________________________
   ____

3. Magneto systems can produce as many as _____ volts.

   3. ________________________

4. The factor that determines the amount of voltage required by the ignition system is the _____ of the spark plug.

   4. ________________________

5. A new spark plug may need only _____ volts to fire.

   5. ________________________

6. You can analyze the quality of combustion that has been taking place in the cylinder by examining the carbon deposits on the _____ _____.

   6. ________________________

7. The spark plug from an engine with normal combustion will show a(n) _____ color on the _____. 7. ____________________

____

8. A spark plug showing erosion of the _____ indicates many hours of use. 8. ____________________

9. List five causes of spark plug deposits.

____

____

____

____

____

10. List the four steps for properly removing a spark plug.

____

____

____

____

11. Gapping of used or worn spark plug electrodes should be done with a(n) _____ type gapping tool. 11. ____________________

12. If spark plug threads are nicked or damaged _____ the plug. 12. ____________________

13. When installing a spark plug, clean the spark plug _____ first. 13. ____________________

14. When gapping a spark plug, you should bend the _____ electrode toward or away from the _____ electrode. 14. ____________________

____

15. When can leaf-type feeler gauges be used to check spark plug electrode gap? ____________________

____

16. Spark plugs will last longer in engines with _____ controlled ignition or _____ discharge ignition systems using unleaded fuel. 16. ____________________

____

17. List four engine conditions that may affect the physical appearance of the firing end of a spark plug.

____

____

____

____

18. If a spark plug is tightened excessively, the _____ will be crushed. 18. ____________________

19. When testing the ignition system, the spark should be strong and a(n) _____ color. 19. ____________________

20. If a spark occurs at the base of the plug but not at the tip, the plug is failing under _____ and it should be replaced. 20. ____________________

Name ________________________________

21. If a spark does not jump a(n) _____ inch gap at the plug tip, but jumps the same gap at the base, the plug is defective.
    a. 5/16
    b. 3/16
    c. 3/4
    d. 1/2

21. ____________________

22. If no spark occurs at the plug tip or at the plug base, the _____ is faulty.

22. ____________________

23. The magneto air gap must be correct or magnetic strength and _____ will be reduced.

23. ____________________

24. List the four major components of a magneto ignition system.

____

____

____

____

25. Name two tools that may be used to remove a flywheel.

____

____

26. List five items that should be examined after removing the flywheel.

____

____

____

____

____

27. Poor fitting or partly sheared flywheel keys can affect _____.

27. ____________________

28. List the conditions that should be checked for after removing the flywheel. ____________________

____

____

____

____

29. A coil's primary windings should be tested for _____ with a(n) _____.

29. ____________________

____

30. The secondary coil should be checked by connecting one probe to the _____ connection and the other probe to the _____ _____ lead.

30. ____________________

____

31. A coil is good if there is _____.
    a. no resistance in either the primary or secondary coil
    b. high resistance in either the primary or secondary coil
    c. high resistance in the primary coil but not in the secondary coil
    d. high resistance in the secondary coil but not in the primary coil

31. ______________________

32. When testing a condenser, the meter should initially show a low _____ and then rise rapidly.

32. ______________________

33. If a solid state system fails to produce a spark between the spark plug cable and the cylinder head, check the condition of the _____.

33. ______________________

34. Special ignition testers can be used to verify the condition and operation of _____, _____ and solid state ignition components.

34. ______________________
____

35. A(n) _____ _____ is used to set the correct gap of breaker points, then the set screw is tightened to lock in the adjustment.

35. ______________________

36. The first two adjustments to be made when adjusting magneto ignition timing should be the _____ gap and _____ height.

36. ______________________
____

37. After disconnecting the coil lead to the points, a continuity tester is connected to the _____ _____ terminal and the _____ _____ point.

37. ______________________
____

38. The stator plate is rotated until the light of the continuity tester goes out indicating the points have _____.
    a. opened
    b. closed

38. ______________________

39. Before replacing the dust cover over the stator plate, place one or two drops of oil on the _____ _____ oiler to reduce wear on the point wear block.

39. ______________________

40. The flywheel can be held with a(n) _____ wrench or a(n) _____ wrench while torquing the flywheel nut.

40. ______________________
____

41. Prior to replacing a cylinder head, it should be checked for _____ on a surface plate.

41. ______________________

42. List the seven problems for which battery ignition systems should be checked prior to beginning an extensive system analysis.

____
____
____
____
____
____
____

Name ______________________________

43. You can identify a battery ignition system by a(n) _____-_____ coil in addition to a battery and a generator. 43. ______________

44. All lawn and garden tractors built after July of 1987 are required to have a(n) _____ _____ system. 44. ______________

45. _____ water should be added to batteries when water is needed. 45. ______________

46. When adding water to a battery, the water level should be _____ the plates. 46. ______________
    a. just above
    b. just below

47. The specific gravity of the electrolyte in a battery is tested with a(n) _____. 47. ______________

48. A battery should be recharged if the specific gravity of the electrolyte is less than _____. 48. ______________

49. When connecting a battery charger to a battery for charging, connect _____. 49. ______________
    a. positive to negative and negative to positive
    b. positive to positive and negative to negative

50. _____ - _____ batteries cannot be checked with a hydrometer. 50. ______________

51. List four safety precautions that should be followed when charging a battery.

    ____

    ____

    ____

    ____

52. A battery used in freezing temperatures should be _____ _____ to prevent the electrolyte from freezing. If the electrolyte freezes, it can cause the battery's case to crack. 52. ______________

53. Temperatures below 0°F can reduce a battery's cranking power to _____ percent of its normal capacity. 53. ______________

54. Only _____ current can be used to charge batteries. 54. ______________

55. A badly _____ battery can sometimes be reclaimed if it is charged very slowly. 55. ______________

56. Battery potential can be severely reduced by _____ or _____ connections. 56. ______________
    ____

57. The thickness (diameter) of copper wire is expressed in gage numbers: the larger the gage number, the _____ the wire size. 57. ______________

58. Starter circuit wire should be _____ gage (minimum). 58. ______________

59. Generally, _____ gage wire (minimum) is used for the charging circuit. 59. ______________

60. List several wire conditions that can cause problems with engine operation. ____________________

____

____

61. The magneto circuit (ground circuit) requires _____ gage wire (minimum). 61. ____________________

62. When an ammeter is used in a battery ignition system, it measures the rate of _____ _____ from the alternator to the battery. 62. ____________________

63. A(n) _____ is a heavy-duty, electromagnetic switch used to handle large amounts of current. 63. ____________________

64. Switches used for small gas engine applications should be _____ to prevent shorting. 64. ____________________

65. A(n) _____ can be used to test most switches for continuity. 65. ____________________

66. How can you detect worn bearings in a starter or generator? ____________________

____

____

67. A generator commutator can be cleaned and deglazed with fine _____ while the engine is running slowly. 67. ____________________

68. Reversing battery polarity on an engine with an alternator can burn out the _____ _____ and _____. 68. ____________________

____

69. During an alternator output test, if the load lamp does not light when connected to the charging terminal and ground, the _____ should be tested next. 69. ____________________

70. What types of alternator systems cause the brightness of an implement's lights to vary with engine speed?

____

____

71. The regulator-rectifier converts _____ to _____ and regulates the current to the battery. 71. ____________________

____

72. DC-only and dual-circuit alternator systems use a(n) _____ to convert ac to dc. 72. ____________________

73. When a new diode harness is installed, the wires should be soldered with _____ _____ solder. 73. ____________________

74. Voltage regulators should *not* be serviced until the engine has been run for about _____ minutes. 74. ____________________

75. Diodes can be tested with a(n) _____. 75. ____________________

76. When testing a diode, current flow should be indicated in _____. 76. ____________________

a. one direction only
b. two directions

77. List the two adjustments that should be made in the current voltage regulator.

____

____

Name ______________________________

78. Closing voltage should be set at least .5 volts _____ than current voltage.
    a. more
    b. less

    78. ______________________

79. List three defects that may occur in the distributor cap.

    ____

    ____

    ____

80. When inspecting the distributor rotor, you should examine the _____ tab and the _____ _____.

    80. ______________________

    ____

81. Most accurate timing of a distributor can be done with a neon _____ _____.

    81. ______________________

82. What three parts of a distributor should be lubricated?

    ____

    ____

    ____

83. In some solid state systems, an adjustment can be made to the air gap between the _____ _____ and the _____ _____ projection.

    83. ______________________

    ____

• Research and write complete answers to the following questions.

84. Describe in detail the procedures for testing the primary and secondary circuits of a coil, and capacitance of a condenser. ____

    ____

    ____

    ____

    ____

    ____

    ____

85. Describe the steps required in timing an engine ignition system.______________________________

    ____

    ____

    ____

    ____

    ____

    ____

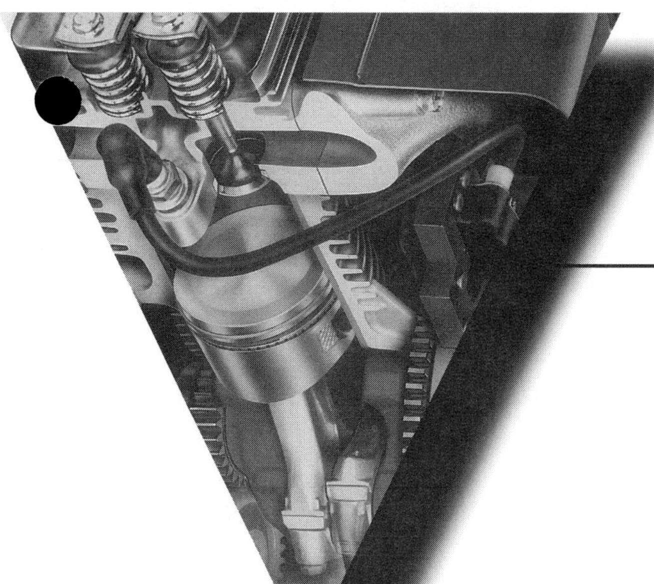

Engine Inspection, Disassembly, and Cylinder Reconditioning

Name________________________________

Date ____________________ Period ____________

Instructor____________________________

After studying this chapter, you will be able to:

- ▼ Inspect engines for problems.
- ▼ Describe the procedure for removing an engine from an implement.
- ▼ List the steps involved in disassembling an engine.
- ▼ Measure cylinder conditions such as wear and out-of-roundness.
- ▼ Explain procedures involved in reboring a cylinder.
- ▼ Summarize the reasons for honing a cylinder.

Instructions: After studying Chapter 15 in the text, complete the following questions and problems.

1. List three safety rules that you should take into consideration before doing repair work on an engine.

____

____

____

2. What document should you have from the engine manufacturer when working on an engine? ____________

____

3. List four problems that might be indicated by wet oil on the outside of the engine.

____

____

____

____

4. If wires need to be disconnected, what can you do to ensure proper reinstallation? ____________________

____

____

5. Before removing or disassembling an engine, a good safety practice to follow would be to remove the _____ _____ first. 5. ____________________

6. Two types of cylinders found on small engines are the integral (one piece) cylinder and the _____ cylinder block. 6. ____________________

7. List eight general external engine parts that should be removed during disassembly.

____

____

____

____

____

____

____

____

8. In the integral cylinder block, the piston must be removed from the _____ of the cylinder. 8. ____________________
   a. top
   b. bottom

9. During inspection, if the cylinder shows a ridge at the top end, the ridge should be removed with a tool called a(n) _____ _____. 9. ____________________

10. The greatest amount of cylinder wear takes place at the _____. 10. ____________________
    a. center
    b. bottom
    c. top

11. Broken fins on the cylinder can lead to _____. 11. ____________________

12. A cylinder will wear to an oval shape 90° to the crankshaft right below the ridge. This wear is due to three contributing factors. Name them. ____________________

____

____

____

13. The first thing to find out when measuring a cylinder is the amount of _____. 13. ____________________

14. Out-of-roundness for small engines is generally limited to _____. 14. ____________________
    a. .002″
    b. .005″
    c. .010″
    d. .015″

Name ____

15. Identify the tools illustrated below.

15. A. ______________________

B. ______________________

C. ______________________

A

B

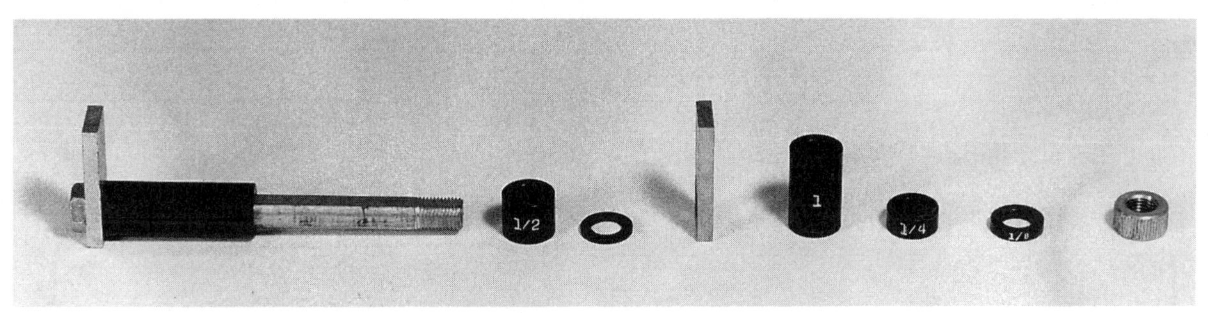

C

16. If cylinder wear is within acceptable limits and no visible damage occurs, a light _____ with a fine emery cloth may be all that is needed.

16. ______________________

17. List two problems that must be solved when reboring a cylinder.

____

____

18. When a cylinder is worn to the point where it needs reboring, the first boring would normally be _____ over the standard size.
    a. .020″
    b. .015″
    c. .1025″
    d. .010″

18. ______________________

19. Cylinder boring machines can be adjusted with a built-in micrometer accurate to _____.
    a. .010″
    b. .001″
    c. .0001″
    d. .00001″

19. ______________________

20. Define honing. ____

____

____

____

21. A typical _____ _____ tool has two abrasive stones and two guides. 21. ____________________

22. Explain why honing is important after boring a cylinder.____________________

23. What operation should follow honing?____________________

• Research and write complete answers to the following questions.

24. Describe the engine conditions that would indicate to a technician that a complete overhaul should be done.

25. After examining an engine's condition, what factors would indicate that a complete overhaul is *not* necessary?

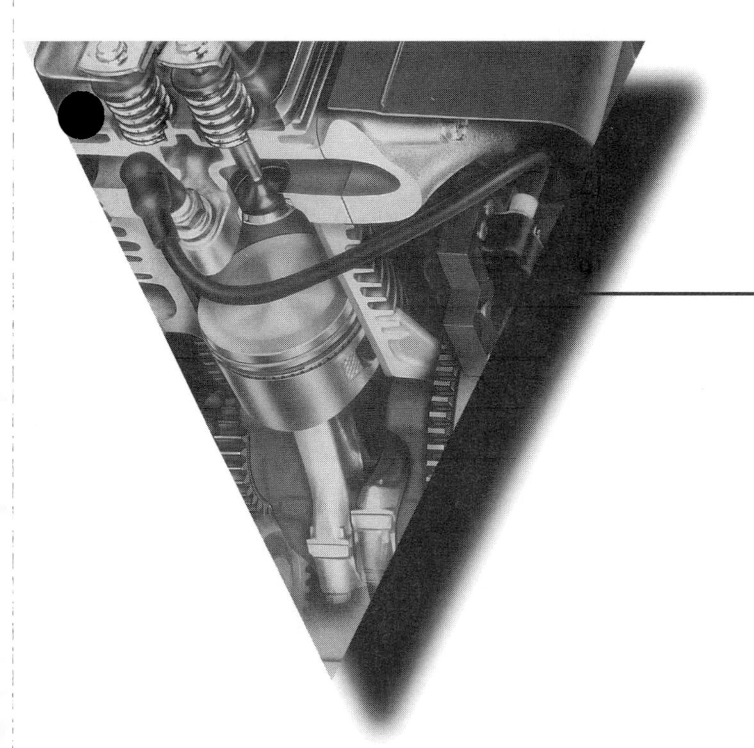

Piston and Piston Ring Service

Name______________________________

Date ________________ Period __________

Instructor___________________________

After studying this chapter, you will be able to:

- Describe piston and piston ring construction.
- Differentiate between compression rings and oil control rings.
- Explain the purpose of ring end gap.
- Identify common types of piston damage and list possible causes.
- Summarize what happens during piston ring wear-in.
- Explain the purpose of a piston pin.

Instructions: After studying Chapter 16 of the text, complete the following questions and problems.

1. List four engine conditions that indicate a possible need for new piston rings.

____

____

____

____

2. The two metals from which pistons are most often made are _____ and _____.   2. ____________________
   ____

3. The ridges between the ring grooves are called _____.   3. ____________________

4. Explain the function of the oil control ring. ______________________________

____

____

5. Identify the parts indicated on the piston below.

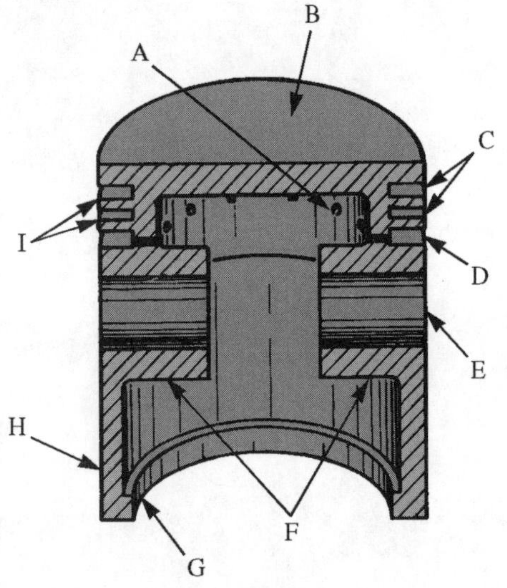

5. A. ____________
B. ____________
C. ____________
D. ____________
E. ____________
F. ____________
G. ____________
H. ____________
I. ____________

6. The _____ is the lightest part of the piston. 6. ____________

7. The section of the piston surrounding the piston pin hole is called the _____ _____. 7. ____________

8. The two main reasons for a specific piston to cylinder clearance is to accommodate _____ _____ and _____. 8. ____________
____

9. When cam ground pistons heat up, they expand _____. 9. ____________
   a. perpendicular to the piston pin
   b. parallel to the piston pin
   c. equally perpendicular and parallel to the piston pin
   d. a lesser amount

10. Thrust surfaces on a piston are at _____ _____ to the centerline of the crankshaft and piston pin. 10. ____________

11. Why is the piston made smaller at the head than at the skirt? ____________
____

12. Draw four common shapes of piston heads on the pistons shown below.

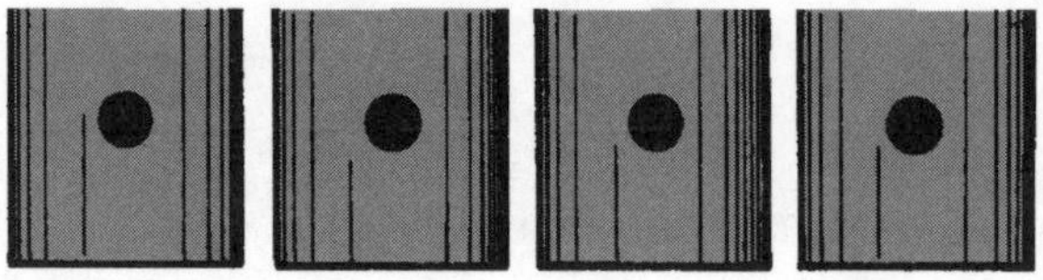

13. Piston rings are separated from the cylinder wall by a thin film of _____. 13. ____________

14. Compression piston rings form a seal by fitting closely to the cylinder wall and the ring _____. 14. ____________

Name ______________________________

15. The sides of a ring groove must have what three characteristics?

____

____

____

16. The piston ring must have proper side _____ in the ring groove. 16. ______________

17. Piston rings may be made of _____ _____ or _____. 17. ______________

____

18. Compression rings are usually made of _____. 18. ______________

19. Why are compression rings designed to twist slightly in the ring grooves? ______________

____

20. Explain why some two-cycle engines have piston rings pinned so they cannot revolve around the ring groove.

____

____

21. Ring side clearance can be checked with a tool called a(n) _____ _____. 21. ______________

22. Piston rings are installed on a piston with a tool called a ring _____. 22. ______________

23. The oil control ring is located at the _____ of a piston. 23. ______________
    a. top
    b. bottom
    c. middle
    d. middle and bottom

24. A general rule for ring end gap is to allow _____ ″ for every inch of cylinder diameter. 24. ______________

25. Piston rings installed with too little end gap will result in broken rings and scored _____ _____. 25. ______________

26. Too much end gap will result in _____. 26. ______________

27. Ring end gap is measured by placing the ring in the cylinder and using a tool called a(n) _____ _____. 27. ______________

28. If the ring end gap is too small, the ring ends can be carefully _____ until the proper gap is obtained. 28. ______________

29. Piston rings are installed on a piston with a tool called a ring _____. 29. ______________

30. When installing a piston with the ring in a cylinder, a tool called a(n) _____ _____ must be used to overcome ring tension. 30. ______________

31. When rings are placed on a piston prior to installing them in a cylinder, the ring gaps should be _____ to obtain the maximum compression. 31. ______________

32. When the _____ becomes greater than .008″ or .010″, the ring tension on the cylinder is lost and the end gaps open wide to allow oil to pass through to the combustion chamber. 32. ____________

33. Tapered cylinders will result in two conditions. They are ____________

____

____________.

34. List seven causes of damaged pistons.

____

____

____

____

____

____

____

35. Rings that are stuck in the ring grooves indicate _____. 35. ____________

36. A hole melted in the face of the piston indicates a serious case of _____. 36. ____________

37. A diagonal wear pattern observed on the piston skirt indicates a misalignment of the piston and the _____ _____. 37. ____________

38. When the piston pin is free to turn in the rod as well as in the piston bosses, it is said to be _____. 38. ____________

39. To increase the wearability of piston pins, they are subjected to a heat treating process called _____ _____. 39. ____________

40. Some piston pins are kept from contacting the cylinder walls with _____ _____ placed in the pin bosses. 40. ____________

41. Press fitted piston pins should be removed with a mechanical or hydraulic _____. 41. ____________

42. If the pin to boss clearance is excessive and an oversize pin is required, the bosses must then be _____. 42. ____________

43. When removing piston pins, snap rings _____. 43. ____________
    a. can be removed with a screwdriver or needle nose pliers
    b. must be removed first
    c. can slip out of the pin boss or the jaws of the pliers
    d. All of the above.

Name ________________________________

• Research and write complete answers to the following questions.

44. Do some research and describe the manufacturing process of piston rings, valves, or pistons used in small engines. ________________________________

45. Examine some very old discarded engine cylinders, pistons and piston rings. Try to interpret the conditions that caused the wear or failure of these components. Compare them with the examples in the text. List your observations below. ________________________________

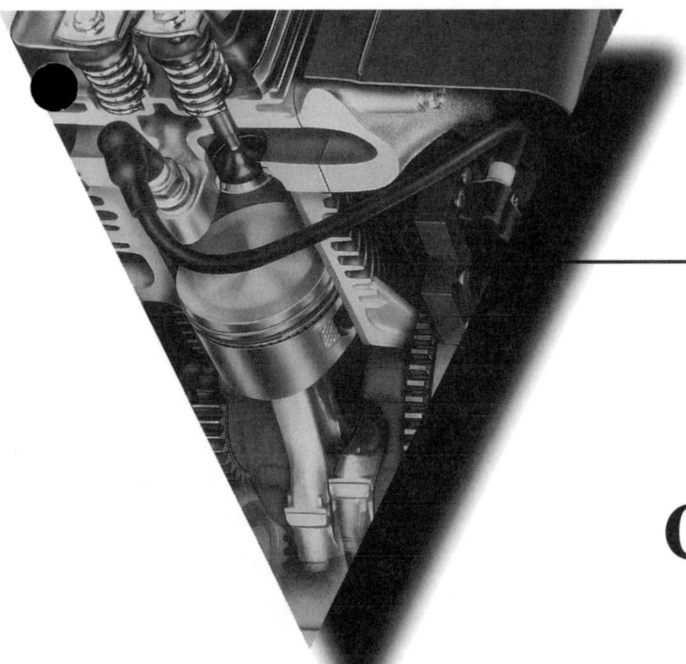

Bearing, Crankshaft, Valve, and Camshaft Service

Name____________________

Date ______________ Period __________

Instructor____________________

After studying this chapter, you will be able to:

- ▼ Describe the function of the connecting rod and the bearings.
- ▼ Define bearing spread and bearing crush.
- ▼ Differentiate between friction bearings and antifriction bearings.
- ▼ Summarize the function of the crankshaft.
- ▼ Service conventional and overhead valve assemblies.
- ▼ Explain the operation of ports, reeds, and rotary valves.
- ▼ Describe the purpose of the camshaft.
- ▼ Explain the purpose of an automatic compression release.

Instructions: After studying Chapter 17 in the text, complete the following questions and problems by writing your answers in the blanks.

1. The _____ _____ attaches the piston to the crankshaft. 1. ____________________
2. _____ are used at both ends of the connecting rod to reduce friction. 2. ____________________
3. Precision insert bearings are prevented from turning in the rod by use of bearing _____. 3. ____________________
4. When installing precision insert bearings in a connecting rod, the proper procedure is to press them into place by exerting pressure at the _____ of the insert. 4. ____________________
5. When insert bearings are manufactured, they are made to a slightly larger curve than the rod bore so that they will seat tightly. This is called bearing _____. 5. ____________________

6. When precision inserts are carefully pressed into the rod bore, the ends will protrude slightly above the parting surface. This is called bearing _____. 6. ____________________
7. Bearing inserts are made in _____ pairs. 7. ____________________
8. Connecting rod caps should never be reversed during assembly. To avoid this possibility, the manufacturer places _____ _____ on the rod and cap. 8. ____________________
9. Rod cap screws should be tightened with a(n) _____ _____ to specified tightness. 9. ____________________
10. Crankshafts may be made of cast steel or _____-_____ steel. 10. ____________________
11. The crankshaft _____ is the offset portion of the shaft measured from the center line to the main bearing bore to the center line of the connecting rod journal. 11. ____________________
12. To reduce vibration, _____ are added to the crankshaft. 12. ____________________
13. Identify the items illustrated below. 13. A. ____________________
B. ____________________
C. ____________________

14. List the three types of main bearings that may be used on small engines.

____

____

____

15. Explain why a specified amount of crankshaft end clearance is necessary. ____________________

____

16. The tool most commonly used to measure the diameter of main bearings and connecting rod journals is a(n) _____. 16. ____________________
17. If the main bearings are machined bores or pressed inserts, the tools most commonly used to measure the bore diameter are a(n) _____ gauge and a(n) _____. 17. ____________________
____
18. When bearings are of the insert type, bearing clearance is measured with a special plastic material called _____. 18. ____________________

Name ______________________________

19. When checking bearing clearance with a plastic strip, the bearing cap must be tightened to the specified _____.

19. ______________________

20. If a crank journal is worn or scored, it will have to be _____ to a specific undersize.

20. ______________________

21. Crankcase _____ prevent leakage of oil from the areas where the crankshaft and crankcase come together.

21. ______________________

22. To keep the sealing lip in contact with the crankshaft surface, a(n) _____ _____ is employed in the seal.

22. ______________________

23. When crankcase seals are properly installed, they take advantage of the engine's internal _____ to keep the seal in contact with the shaft.

23. ______________________

24. When sliding an oil seal on or off the crankshaft, it must be protected from the sharp edges of the _____.

24. ______________________

25. Before installing an oil seal, a liquid _____ should be applied to the outside of the shell of the seal.

25. ______________________

26. Identify the parts of the oil seal shown below.

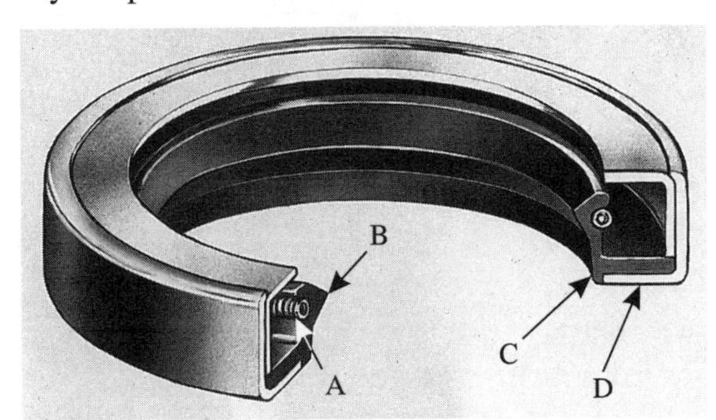

26. A. ______________________
B. ______________________
C. ______________________
D. ______________________

27. Identify the parts of the poppet valve assembly shown below.

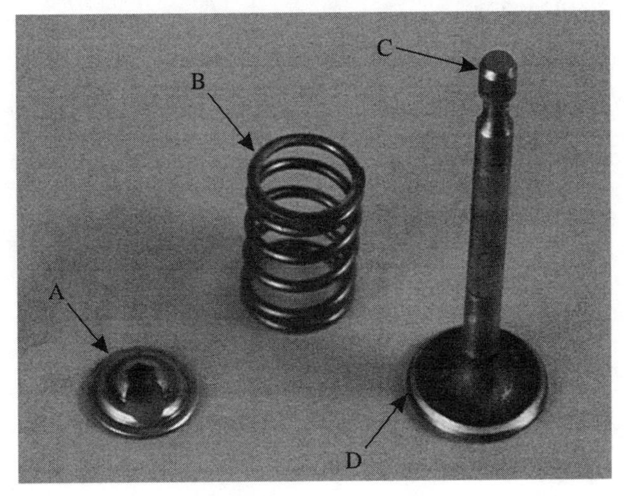

27. A. ______________________
B. ______________________
C. ______________________
D. ______________________

28. To remove a keeper from a valve, a special tool is required called a valve _____ _____.

28. ______________________

29. List six possible valve defects that should be included in the inspection of a used valve.

____

____

____

____

____

____

30. Poor fuel flow into the cylinders past the valve can be caused by excess _____. 30. ______________

31. List three things to examine when testing valve springs.

____

____

____

32. A worn valve guide may allow the valve to _____, thus allowing exhaust leakage. 32. ______________

33. Normal guide to valve stem clearance is usually about _____. 33. ______________
   a. .002″–.006″
   b. .001″–.002″
   c. .002″–.003″
   d. .003″–.005″

34. If integral valve guides are used and found to be irregular, they can be _____ to fit an oversize valve stem. 34. ______________

35. After a valve guide has been cleaned with a special wire brush, the inside diameter can be measured with a tool called a(n) _____ _____ gauge and a micrometer. 35. ______________

36. Some engines have valve guides that are _____. 36. ______________

37. When reaming valve guides, it is important to rotate the reamer in the _____ direction when removing it. 37. ______________

38. It is extremely important to wash away any _____ after valve guide reaming. 38. ______________

39. Briggs & Stratton valve guides are coded by _____ and _____ on the guides. 39. ______________

____

40. What two results may occur if a valve seat is too narrow?

____

____

41. A valve seat that is too wide may not seat due to _____ on the seat. 41. ______________

42. A valve seat that does not seat will warp and _____. 42. ______________

Name ______________________________

43. Specified valve seat widths normally range from _____.
    a. .030″–.060″
    b. .020″–.040″
    c. .030″–.040″
    d. .010″–.020″

43. ______________________

44. On some engines, valve seat _____ can be removed and installed.

44. ______________________

45. To counterbore for a new insert, a special counterbore is needed with a proper _____ to guide it.

45. ______________________

46. When installing a new insert, the _____ side should be facing toward the _____ of the hole.

46. ______________________

____

47. The valve seating line on the valve should be located _____ of the face.
    a. near the top
    b. anywhere between top and bottom
    c. near the bottom
    d. near the center

47. ______________________

48. A valve seat grinder or cutting tool must be guided with a(n) _____ fastened in the valve guide.

48. ______________________

49. Valve lapping is done with a coarse _____ _____ abrasive combined with a special grease.

49. ______________________

50. A tool called a(n) _____ _____ has a suction cup that attaches to the valve head.

50. ______________________

51. List the five main steps of hand lapping a valve.

____

____

____

____

____

52. Valve refacing can be done on a _____.
    a. special valve grinder
    b. valve lathe
    c. manual valve refacer
    d. All of the above.

52. ______________________

53. A valve grinding machine can, in addition to refacing a valve, grind the ends of valve _____ and _____.

53. ______________________

____

54. Identify the components of the complete valve train illustrated below.

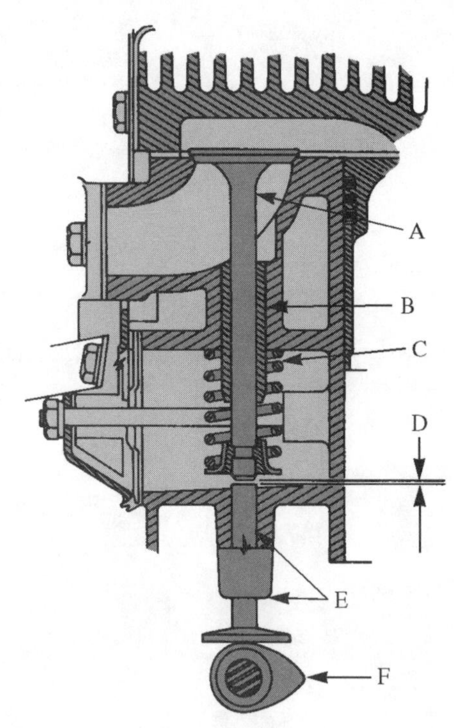

54. A. ____________________
B. ____________________
C. ____________________
D. ____________________
E. ____________________
F. ____________________

55. An overhead valve system transmits motion from the camshaft to the valves through _____ and _____ _____.

55. ____________________
____

56. Overhead valve systems improve _____ efficiency and eliminate combustion chamber _____ _____.

56. ____________________
____

57. Identify the parts of the overhead valve system shown below.

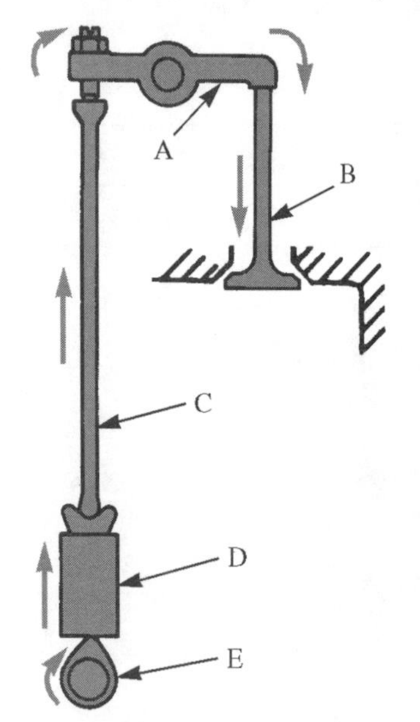

57. A. ____________________
B. ____________________
C. ____________________
D. ____________________
E. ____________________

Name ______________________________

58. To remove valve springs from some overhead valve engines, a tool called a valve _____ _____ is required to extract the retainers. 58. ______________________

59. Valve guides that are out of tolerance should be _____ out of the cylinder head. New valve guides should be installed to the manufacturer's specified _____. 59. ______________________ ______________________

60. When inserting valves into guides, a valve guide _____ should be applied to the valve stems. 60. ______________________

61. Rocker arms should not be installed until after the _____ _____ is attached to the block. 61. ______________________

62. Valve clearance must be adjusted to the manufacturer's specifications. Excessive valve clearance will reduce _____ _____. Insufficient valve clearance can cause valve ____ or _____. 62. ______________________ ______________________ ______________________

63. Why do some engine manufacturers specify different valve clearance settings for the intake and exhaust valves? ____
____
____

64. The tool used to measure valve clearance settings is called a(n) _____ _____. 64. ______________________

65. Too little valve clearance can result in a burned valve _____ and _____. 65. ______________________ ______________________

66. Insufficient clearance will cause valve timing to be _____. 66. ______________________
   a. advanced
   b. retarded

67. Too much valve clearance will alter valve timing and _____ valve lift. 67. ______________________
   a. increase
   b. decrease

68. Valve stem-to-lifter clearance is measured with a(n) _____ gauge. 68. ______________________

69. If the engine does not have adjustable tappets, the valve clearance can be increased by grinding a small amount from the _____ _____. 69. ______________________

70. Instead of poppet valves, two-cycle engines generally use a(n) _____ system for intake and exhaust flow. 70. ______________________

71. Reed valves are used in _____ -cycle engines to control _____ flow. 71. ______________________ ______________________

72. Reed valves are operated by an internal engine _____. 72. ______________________

73. To prevent excessive reed flexing and distortion, a reed _____ is fastened to the reed plate. 73. ______________________

74. The camshaft is driven by the crankshaft and rotates _____ as the crankshaft.
    a. twice as fast
    b. one-half as fast
    c. the same speed
    d. one-fourth as fast

74. _______________

75. The part of the cam that contacts the valve lifter is the _____.

75. _______________

76. The crankshaft gear and camshaft gear have _____ marks that must be aligned when installing the cam.

76. _______________

77. The _____ _____ release mechanism lifts the exhaust valve a small amount during cranking and releases part of the compression pressure.

77. _______________

78. Once the engine begins to run, the automatic compression release is disengaged by _____ _____.

78. _______________

• Research and write complete answers to the following questions.

79. Describe the parts of overhead valve systems and how they work. _______________

80. How does a camshaft function and how does it contribute to valve timing? _______________

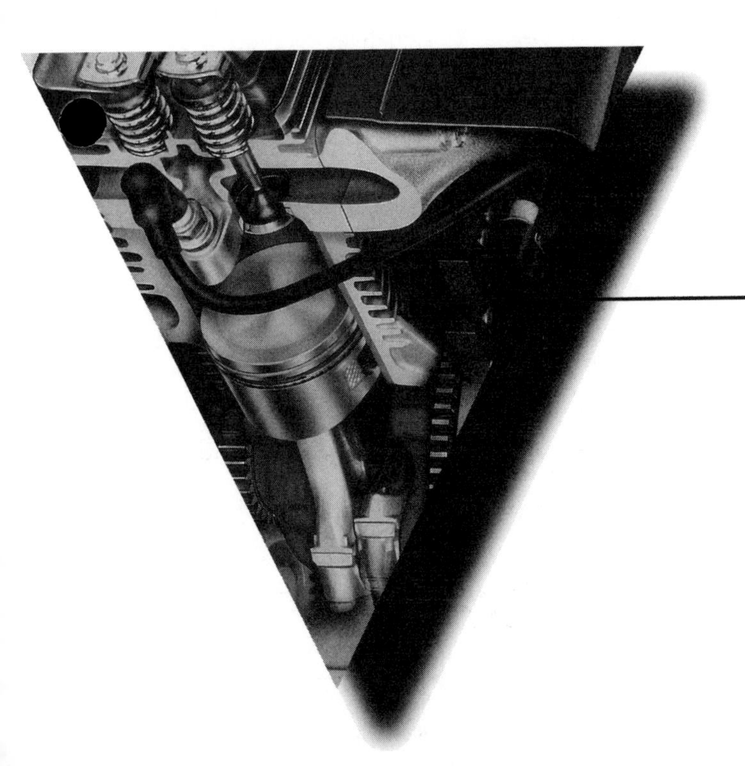

Lawn Equipment

Name______________________________

Date ________________ Period __________

Instructor_________________________

After studying this chapter, you will be able to:

- ▼ List and conform to safe work practices.
- ▼ List features to consider when purchasing a lawn mower.
- ▼ Summarize basic lawn mower maintenance procedures and safety precautions.
- ▼ Describe proper method for storing a lawn mower for long periods of time.
- ▼ List the features to consider when purchasing a chain saw, a leaf blower, a string trimmer, or an edger/trimmer.
- ▼ Summarize the maintenance, safety, and storage procedures for chain saws, string trimmers, brushcutters, and edger/trimmers.
- ▼ Identify a variety of cutting blades for trimmers and brushcutters.

Instructions: After studying Chapter 18 of the text, complete the following questions and problems.

1. What safety action should always be done before servicing the engine on a lawn mower, or other lawn equipment?
____

2. Gasoline should always be stored in _____ gasoline containers. 2. ______________

3. Lawn mowers have caused a great number of injuries. The most severe injuries recorded are lacerations to the _____ and _____. 3. ______________ ______________

4. It has been reported that objects have been thrown from a lawn mower as far as _____. 4. ______________

5. Each year more than _____ lawn mower injuries are treated by hospitals. 5. ______________

6. The most frequent victims of lawn mower accidents are under the age of _____. 6. ______________________ _____

7. The *Knowing Mowing* program has been created by the _____ _____ and the _____ _____ Corporation. 7. ______________________ __
____

8. The *Knowing Mowing* program is designed to teach youngsters _____ years and older to safely _____ and _____ lawn mowers. 8. ______________________
____
____

9. The operator's strength might determine whether he/she should purchase a(n) _____ or _____ lawn mower. 9. ______________________
____

10. The lawn mower that has horizontally rotating blades is called a(n) _____ lawn mower. 10. ______________________

11. The type of lawn mower that produces the highest quality job and has helical cutting blades is the _____-type mower. 11. ______________________

12. For the average size yard, a rotary mower with a(n) _____ inch blade is usually satisfactory. 12. ______________________

13. For small yards a blade length of _____ inches is more maneuverable and takes less storage space. 13. ______________________

14. Cutting height is lessened by _____. 14. ______________________
    a. lowering the engine and blade
    b. raising the engine and blade
    c. lowering the wheels
    d. raising the wheels

15. Self-propelled mowers can be driven from the engine by _____. 15. ______________________
    a. shafts and gears
    b. a belt and pulley system
    c. Either a or b.
    d. Neither a nor b.

16. Which engine type has fewer moving parts? 16. ______________________
    a. Four-cycle engine
    b. Two-cycle engine

17. Which type of engine requires that a special oil be mixed with the fuel before placing it in the fuel tank? 17. ______________________
    a. Two-cycle engine
    b. Four-cycle engine

18. Without oil in the fuel, a two-cycle engine will be ruined in a few _____. 18. ______________________

19. For catching grass cuttings, either a(n) _____ bag, or _____ bag is available. 19. ______________________
____

20. Grass cuttings are excellent material for _____. 20. ______________________

21. If a grass catching device is not used, the cut grass should be _____. 21. ______________________

22. Grass cuttings that are left in the lawn are called _____. 22. ______________________

Name ____

23. A device that removes residual grass cuttings from the lawn is called a(n) _____. 23. ____________________________

24. Some mowers are designed to cut blades of grass into fine particles called _____ which decomposes into fertilizer. 24. ____________________________

25. When tipping a lawn mower on its side for cleaning, always have the _____ facing _____. 25. ____________________________

____

26. When removing a rotary lawnmower blade for sharpening, the first thing to do is remove the spark plug wire and ____

____.

27. You should wear _____ when removing blade bolts. 27. ____________________________

28. List the five kinds of engine starters that have been used on lawnmower engines.

____

____

____

____

____

29. Every lawn mower manufactured today is required to have a braking system that will stop the blade within _____ seconds after the operator's hands leave the handle. 29. ____________________________

30. Identify the parts indicated in the illustration below. 30. A. ____________________________

B. ____________________________

C. ____________________________

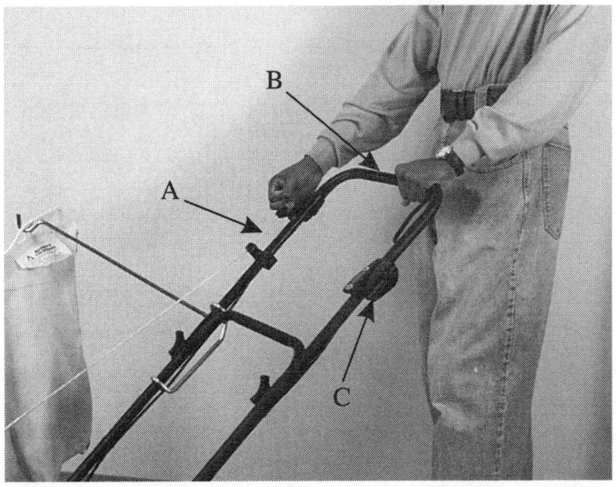

31. List the six steps for starting a lawn mower engine.

____

____

____

____

____

____

32. For restarting a warm engine, _____ or _____ should *not* be necessary. 32. ______________________________

____

33. If the idle speed is too fast or slow the carburetor can be adjusted with a(n) _____. 33. ______________________________

34. If there is a good spark between the high tension wire and the engine but no spark at the spark plug, you should _____ or _____ the spark plug. 34. ______________________________

____

35. If there is no spark between the high tension wire and the engine, you should refer to a(n) _____ _____. 35. ______________________________

36. Blades, when dull or nicked, can be sharpened by _____. 36. ______________________________

37. During sharpening, the blade should also be balanced to avoid damaging vibration. Always wear safety _____ when grinding or filing a blade. 37. ______________________________

38. Hitting hard objects while mowing can cause damage to the mower. List five parts that can receive damage.

____

____

____

____

____

39. When installing a spark plug it is important not to _____ it. 39. ______________________________

40. Air cleaners should be cleaned or replaced every _____ hours. 40. ______________________________

41. List the six steps for cleaning an oil-wetted air cleaner.

____

____

____

____

____

42. Four-cycle engines should have the oil changed about every _____ hours. 42. ______________________________

43. List the five steps for draining oil from a lawn mower engine.

____

____

____

____

____

44. List the three steps for replacing engine oil.

____

____

____

Name ______________________________

45. When replacing a screw-in type muffler the threads should be coated with a(n) _____ compound. 45. ______________

46. Rayon cord V-belts will not last as long as _____ cord V-belts. 46. ______________

47. Polyester cord V-belts could be dangerous due to their tendency to _____ when they get hot. 47. ______________

48. A lawn mower will operate safely and reliably for many years if it is _____ according to the ten suggestions in the text. 48. ______________

49. Although it is best to run the engine dry of fuel before storing it, fuel can be left in the tank if a fuel _____ is added. 49. ______________

50. Chain saws are manufactured in sizes from about _____ inches to over _____ inches of blade length. 50. ______________
____

51. List four factors that should be considered when purchasing a chain saw.

____

____

____

____

52. A safety device for chain saws that prevents kickback is a(n) _____ _____. 52. ______________

53. Another safety device used to prevent injury from kickback is the _____ _____ device near the handle grip. 53. ______________

54. When carrying a chain saw the engine must be _____ and the _____ should be positioned away from the side of the body. 54. ______________
____

55. List five rules for avoiding chain saw kickback.

____

____

____

____

____

56. Clogged cylinder fins will cause engine _____. 56. ______________

57. Before removing the air filter for cleaning, it is recommended that you close the _____ _____. 57. ______________

58. Chain saw fuel filters are located at the end of a(n) _____ _____ tube. 58. ______________

59. The fuel filter on a chain saw has to come out through the _____ _____ cap. 59. ______________

60. On chain saws there is a(n) _____ _____ system to lubricate the guide bar and chain. 60. ______________

61. List seven major parts of a chain saw that need periodic inspection and/or service.

____

____

____

____

____

____

____

62. A loop-type handle should *never* be used for cutting blades on _____. 62. _______________

63. The most basic cutting end is the rotating _____ cutting head. 63. _______________

64. For brushcutting, either a(n) _____ or _____ handle should be used. 64. _______________ _______________

65. List six basic wearing apparel items that are recommended for safe operation of string trimmers and brushcutters.

____

____

____

____

____

____

66. String trimmers and brushcutter engines are _____. 66. _______________
   a. four-cycle
   b. two-cycle
   c. four and two-cycle

67. When cutting young saplings, the sapling should be on the _____ side of the cutter as seen from the operators position. 67. _______________

68. Other than the engine, the flexible _____ _____ and, _____ on some models, may need greasing. 68. _______________ _______________

69. When starting a walk-behind combination edger/trimmer for lawn care, it is important that the _____ always be _____. 69. _______________ _______________

70. The blade on combination edger/trimmers is driven by a(n) _____ from the engine. 70. _______________

71. When operating an edger/trimmer, proper clothing and _____ protection is necessary. 71. _______________

72. Edger blades are _____ when they wear down. 72. _______________
   a. sharpened
   b. replaced

73. During edger/trimmer storage the _____ should be loosened. 73. _______________

Name ______________________________

• Research and write complete answers to the following questions.

74. Describe the type of things that would be most important to you if you were purchasing a new lawn mower.

75. List engine maintenance that is common to all equipment described in this chapter. List those items that are unique to each kind of equipment described in this chapter.

Lawn and Garden Tractors

Name________________________________

Date ____________________ Period ____________

Instructor______________________________

After studying this chapter, you will be able to:

- ▼ Describe tractor operating safety.
- ▼ List features to look for when purchasing a lawn and garden tractor.
- ▼ List the various kinds of work done with lawn and garden tractors.
- ▼ Identify principles of good design for lawn and garden tractors.
- ▼ Describe the kinds of accessories that can be used with lawn and garden tractors.
- ▼ Identify several transmission systems used for lawn and garden tractors.
- ▼ Describe electrical systems and components used on lawn and garden tractors.

Instructions: After studying Chapter 19 of the text, complete the following questions and problems.

1. Lawn and garden tractors are generally _____ than farm tractors. 1. ______________________

2. All _____ _____ should be read and understood before attempting to operate a lawn or garden tractor. 2. ______________________

3. Safety signs and _____ should all be read and understood before operating a lawn or garden tractor. 3. ______________________

4. A tractor operator should never carry _____ or let them ride on a tractor or attachment. 4. ______________________

5. A lawn and garden tractor operator should never wear _____ _____ while operating a machine. 5. ______________________

6. Name at least eight items of appropriate protective clothing that a lawn and garden tractor operator should wear.

7. List eight considerations that the operator should be aware of during mowing.

8. What precautions should be taken before dismounting a tractor?

9. To avoid some of the most severe injuries, keep _____, _____, and _____ away from mower when engine is running.

9. __________

10. When not mowing, the mower blades should be _____.

10. __________

11. List the procedures for parking a tractor safely.

Name ____

12. If a tractor stops going forward uphill, the corrective action is to _____. 12. ____________________
    a. turn around quickly
    b. back up while making a 180° turn
    c. back straight slowly to the bottom of the hill
    d. jump from the tractor and let it go

13. A tractor should be placed on a(n) _____ for towing. 13. ____________________

14. A tractor should be loaded on a trailer or truck carefully with strong, wide _____. 14. ____________________

15. List the seven most common uses of garden tractors.

____

____

____

____

____

____

____

16. A large mower deck means fewer trips, which equates to less _____. 16. ____________________
    a. time spent mowing
    b. fuel consumption
    c. engine maintenance
    d. All of the above.

17. In order to move the cut grass from the deck to the container at the rear of the tractor, a(n) _____ _____ and strong _____ is installed on the tractor. 17. ____________________
    ____

18. Grass can be cut into very fine particles with a special _____ blade. 18. ____________________

19. When mulching it is best to cut only _____ of the blade of grass. 19. ____________________

20. Mulching requires _____. 20. ____________________
    a. more power
    b. less power
    c. the same power
    d. faster speed

21. A straight concave blade can be attached to the front of the tractor for plowing _____. 21. ____________________

22. Snow throwers can be attached to the front of the tractor and directed to the _____. 22. ____________________
    a. right side
    b. left side
    c. straight ahead
    d. All of the above.

23. To achieve greater traction on slippery surfaces, _____ and _____ can be placed on the rear wheels. 23. ______________________ ______________________

24. Snow throwers for tractors may be of the _____ type. 24. ______________________
    a. single-stage
    b. two-stage
    c. Both a and b.

25. In general, front end loading requires a tractor with _____. 25. ______________________
    a. greater horsepower
    b. about the same horsepower
    c. more weight on the front
    d. greater speed

26. Nearly all engines for lawn and garden tractors are _____. 26. ______________________
    a. two-cycle engines with overhead valves
    b. four-cycle engines with reed valves
    c. four-cycle engines with overhead valves and electric start
    d. two-cycle engines with rotary valves and electric start

27. Tractors from 14 to 22 horsepower generally have two cylinders of either the _____ or _____ configuration. 27. ______________________ ______________________

28. List seven components of a standard air-cooled lawn and garden tractor with which the operator should be familiar.

____

____

____

____

____

____

____

29. What additional components would a liquid-cooled tractor have?______________________

____

____

____

____

____

30. The main framework of a tractor is called the chassis which must withstand _____ and _____ forces. 30. ______________________ ______________________

31. Some tractors have _____ _____ steering for greater maneuverability around trees and shrubs. 31. ______________________

Name ________________________________

32. The rear wheel drive unit for a tractor with four wheel steering consists of _____.
    a. axles and universal joints
    b. transmission and input shaft
    c. steering brackets
    d. All of the above.

32. ____________________

33. The variable-speed transmission uses a torque converter with two V-belt pulleys having a moveable portion called a(n) _____.

33. ____________________

34. Variable-speed transmissions are also used on such implements as _____ _____, and some rotary _____.

34. ____________________
____

35. Speed is changed through the variable speed pulley by applying pressure to a(n) _____ _____.

35. ____________________

36. Name the various parts of the four wheel steering assembly illustrated below.

36. A. ____________________
B. ____________________
C. ____________________
D. ____________________
E. ____________________
F. ____________________
G. ____________________

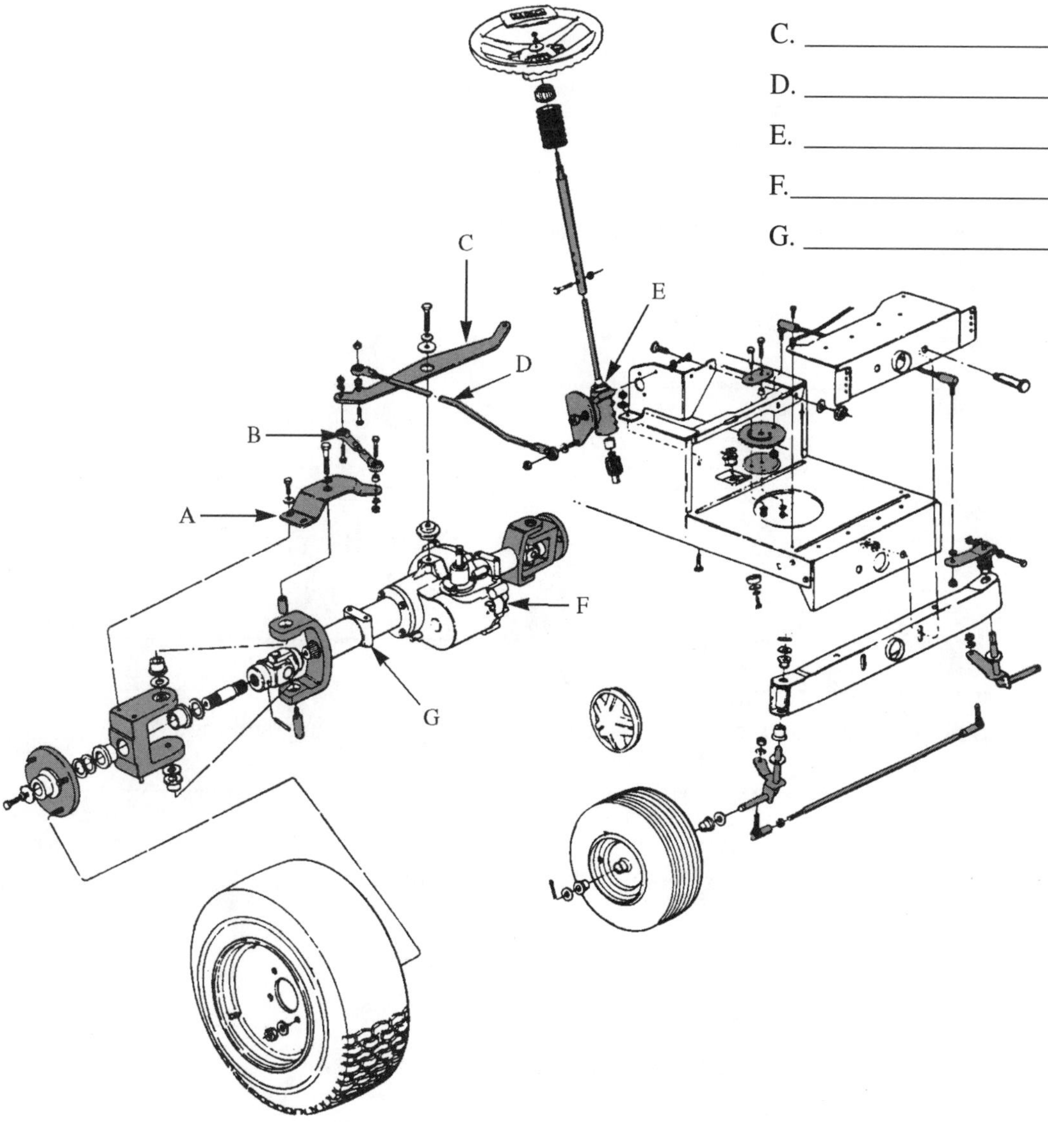

A
B
C
D
E
F
G

37. Name the parts of the variable-speed drive system in the illustration below.

37. A. _______________
B. _______________
C. _______________
D. _______________
E. _______________
F. _______________
G. _______________
H. _______________
I. _______________

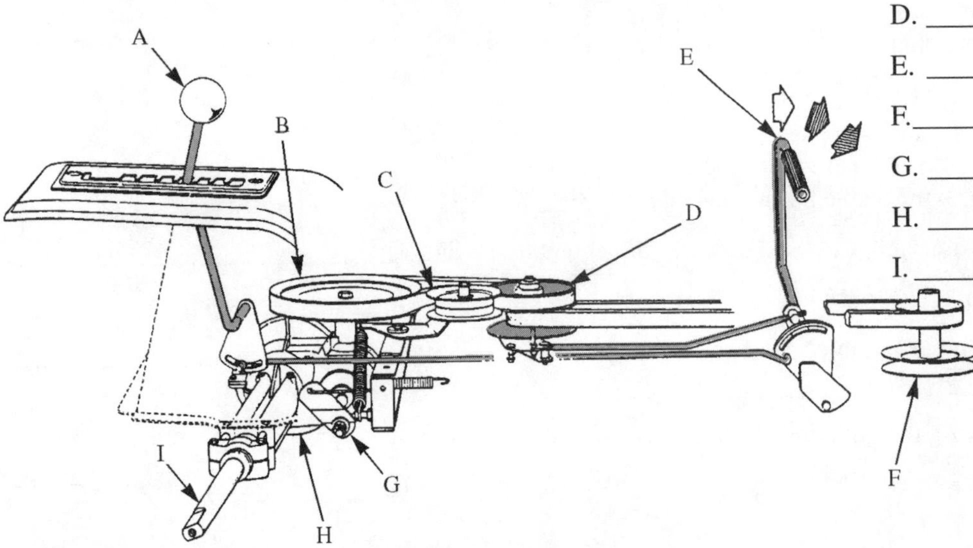

38. Some tractors are _____ _____ driven instead of belt driven from the engine.

38. _______________

39. List the nine advantages hydrostatic transmissions have over variable-speed drive systems.

____
____
____
____
____
____
____
____
____

40. Why should oil *not* be filled to the top of the reservoir on hydrostatic transmissions? _______________
____
____

41. The hydrostatic transmission has a series of ball _____ that pump oil.

41. _______________

42. A hydrostatic transmission consists of a variable displacement _____, and a fixed displacement _____.

42. _______________
____

43. To vary the displacement of a hydrostatic transmission, a(n) _____ _____ is pivoted by a(n) _____ _____.

43. _______________
____

Name ______________________________

44. Assume the engine is running at a fixed rpm and the tractor is slowed by the control lever. In this case the torque at the axles will _____. 44. ______________
    a. decrease as the tractor speed decreases
    b. stay the same with this system
    c. increase as the tractor speed decreases
    d. only increase if the engine rpm is increased

45. A check valve in the system allows fluid to flow in _____. 45. ______________
    a. one direction only
    b. two directions
    c. no direction
    d. all directions at once

46. How is the hydrostatic transmission cooled? ______________

    ____

47. How does a transaxle allow both driving wheels to turn at different speeds while turning corners?

    ____

48. What two things might be the cause of a tractor with a hydrostatic transmission having no output torque in one direction?

    ____

    ____

49. The operator present safety requirement was established in 1987 by the _____ _____ _____ Institute. 49. ______________

50. Safety seat electrical systems are devised so that when the operator leaves the seat, the _____ stops. 50. ______________

51. Some tractors have a oil low _____ switch and an oil low level switch that activate indicator _____ on the instrument panel. 51. ______________

    ____

52. Tractors have electrical systems that include a(n) _____ and _____ charging system. 52. ______________

    ____

53. In an unregulated electrical system, the headlights will dim when the engine _____. 53. ______________
    a. slows down
    b. speeds up

54. List the steps for checking an operator present system (safety seat).

    ____

    ____

    ____

    ____

    ____

55. If, after testing the safety seat system, the engine continues to run, what should be checked next?

____

____

56. If the spark plug high tension lead shows brittleness and cracks in the insulation it is probably due to _____ and _____.

56. _______________

____

57. When draining engine oil, the engine should be run long enough to _____ the oil to thin it for more complete drainage.

57. _______________

58. When installing a new oil filter cartridge, you should apply a film of oil to the _____ and tighten it _____ turns with a filter wrench after it is hand tightened.

58. _______________

____

59. When replacing engine oil always use the correct _____ and _____ service type.

59. _______________

____

60. Although the time for air filter service may vary with operating conditions, the normal time is about every _____ hours.

60. _______________

61. The muffler is a sound deadening device and it increases engine efficiency by controlling exhaust _____ _____.

61. _______________

62. When cleaning dirt from a tractor engine, _____ from a garden hose may be used. A commercial engine _____ _____ may be used if oil is mixed with the dirt.

62. _______________

____

63. When adding or replacing coolant, a mixture of _____ solution should be used. This will lower the freezing point to –34°F and raise the boiling point to 265°F.
   a. 75% water and 25% ethylene glycol
   b. 35% water and 65% ethylene glycol
   c. 40% water and 60% ethylene glycol
   d. 50% water and 50% ethylene glycol

63. _______________

64. A rust _____ will help keep the cooling system clean and free from rust.

64. _______________

65. Corrosive material found on battery terminals can be dissolved and washed away with _____ cup of baking soda mixed in _____ of water.

65. _______________

____

66. A maintenance free battery _____ replaced with a lead-acid battery.
   a. should *never* be
   b. can be
   c. should be
   d. None of the above.

66. _______________

67. If a tractor is to be stored for more than thirty days, a fuel _____ should be added and the engine run for at least _____ minutes.

67. _______________

____

68. It is good practice to _____ the fuel shut-off valve when storing a tractor.
   a. open
   b. close
   c. It makes no difference.

68. _______________

Name ______________________________

• Research and write complete answers to the following questions.

69. Examine the illustration of the two-speed transmission below and explain how it functions with the variable speed pulleys.

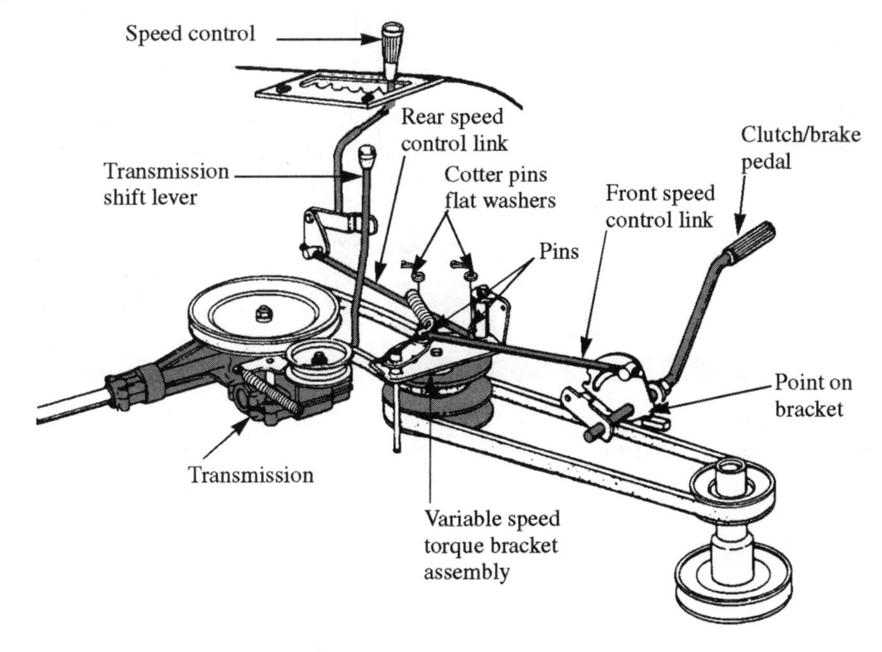

____

____

____

____

____

____

____

____

____

____

____

____

____

70. Study the diagram of the hydrostatic transmission system below and explain how it provides forward, reverse, braking, and free-wheeling functions.

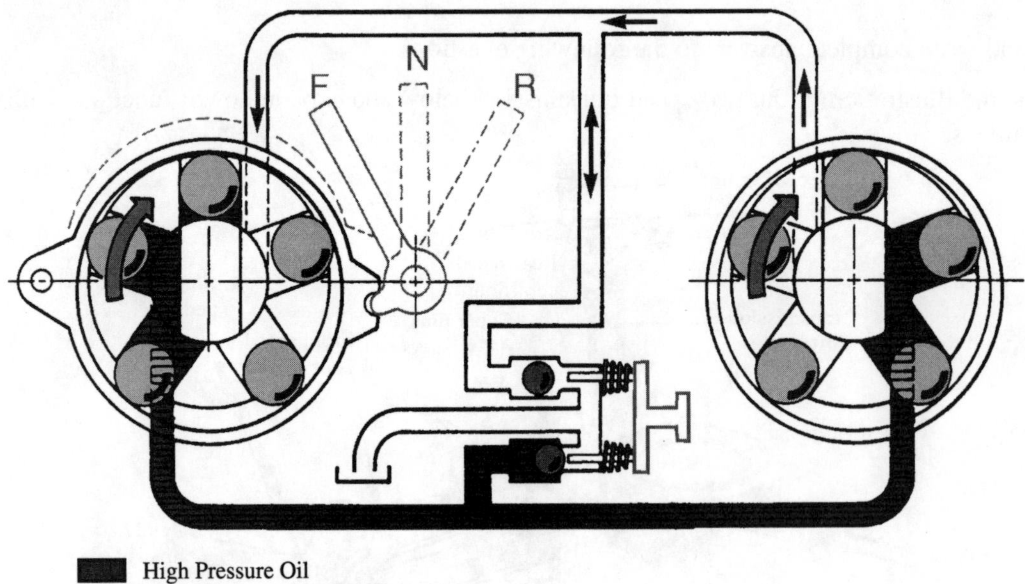

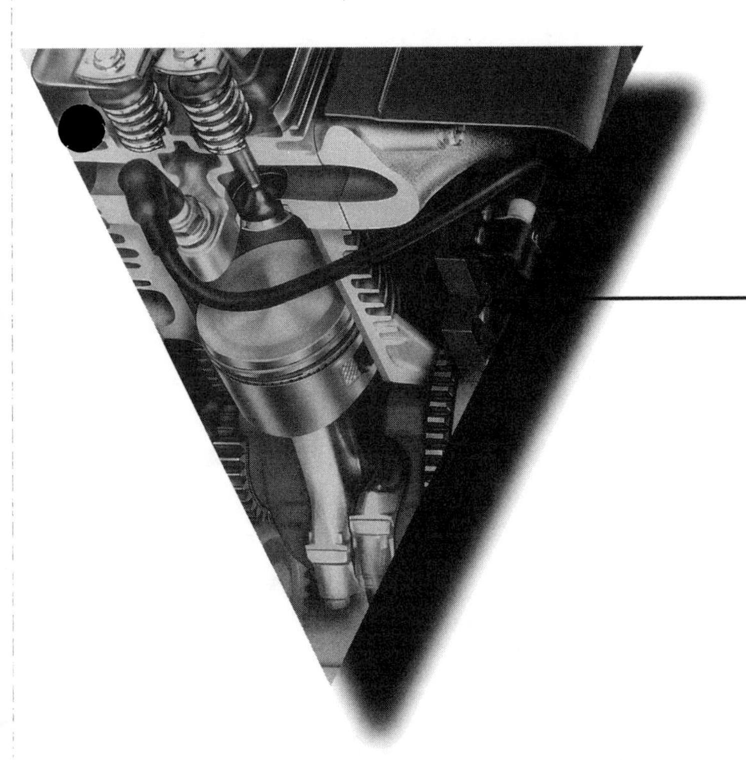

Snow Throwers

Name______________________________

Date ____________________ Period __________

Instructor___________________________

After studying this chapter, you will be able to:

- ▼ Safely operate and service snow throwing equipment.
- ▼ List important purchasing considerations for snow throwers.
- ▼ Identify major parts of walk behind snow throwers.
- ▼ Make adjustments to snow throwers.
- ▼ Properly maintain snow throwing machines.

Instructions: After studying Chapter 20 in the text, complete the following questions and problems.

1. Good _____ must always be used when operating or working with any power equipment. 1. ____________________

2. The operator of a snow thrower must always be alert for _____ and never allow them to operate a snow thrower. 2. ____________________

3. List five safety precautions that should be taken into account when operating a snow thrower.

   ____

   ____

   ____

   ____

   ____

4. Before using a snow thrower you should inspect the machine to be sure all hardware is tight and all damaged or badly worn parts have been _____ or _____. 4. ____________________

   ____

5. If a child or pet enters the work area you should _____ the machine and direct them to a safe area. 5. _______________

6. Small snow throwers for light snow falls and small areas are generally _____. 6. _______________
   a. 10″–12″ in width and about 2 hp
   b. 12″–15″ in width and about 4 hp
   c. 16″–20″ in width and about 3 hp
   d. 20″–22″ in width and about 3 hp

7. Almost all small machines have _____ (rope) start. 7. _______________

8. Small snow throwers are single-stage with _____ or _____ blades that rotate like paddles. 8. _______________
____

9. Direction of snow throwing is controlled by the _____ _____. 9. _______________

10. Midsize snow throwers have _____ engines with 3 to 8 horsepower. 10. _______________
    a. four-cycle
    b. two-cycle
    c. either two- or four-cycle

11. Midsize snow throwers have wheels with _____ tires and heavy _____. 11. _______________
____

12. Proper _____ _____ can improve traction and minimize tire wear. 12. _______________

13. On some models, one or both _____ can be engaged to propel the machine. 13. _______________

14. Augers on mid-sized snow throwers are _____-_____ steel that _____ the snow into the machine. 14. _______________
____

15. Some augers have _____ edges to help break up ice and snow before feeding it into the _____ stage blower. 15. _______________
____

16. Heavy-duty snow throwers are from _____. 16. _______________
    a. 2–3 hp
    b. 5–10 hp
    c. 8–20 hp
    d. 25–30 hp

17. Heavy-duty snow throwers are _____-_____, two-stage machines. 17. _______________

18. Large pneumatic tires are common to heavy-duty machines and cleated _____ are used on some of the larger models. 18. _______________

19. Snow can be thrown as far as _____ feet, and is controllable by a(n) _____ at the top of the direction chute. 19. _______________
____

20. On some models the weight can be shifted by moving the _____. 20. _______________

Name ____

21. Identify the operator controls shown in the illustration below.

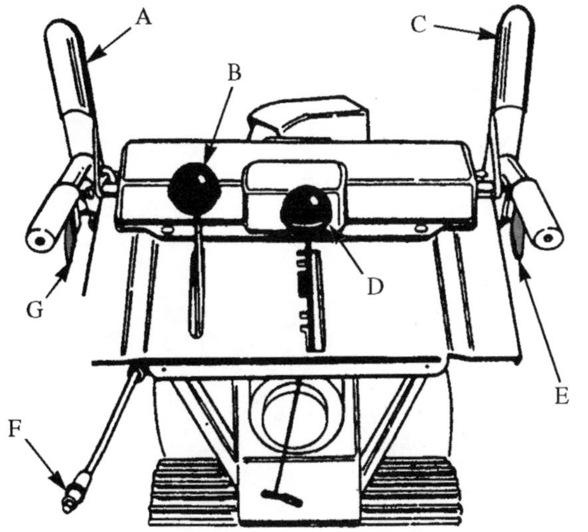

21. A. ____________________________
    B. ____________________________
    C. ____________________________
    D. ____________________________
    E. ____________________________
    F. ____________________________
    G. ____________________________

22. Identify the engine controls shown in the illustration below.

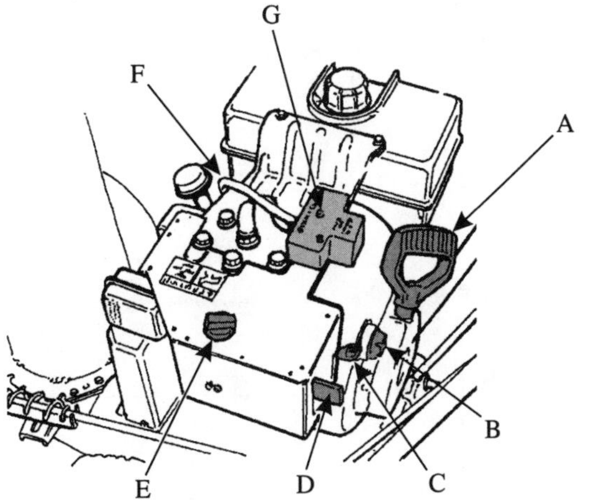

22. A. ____________________________
    B. ____________________________
    C. ____________________________
    D. ____________________________
    E. ____________________________
    F. ____________________________
    G. ____________________________

23. Snow throwers that have electric starters also have a back-up _____.
    a. kick starter
    b. crank starter
    c. inertia starter
    d. recoil starter

23. ____________________________

24. Self-propelled snow throwers will have two separate drive systems. One system drives the auger, or auger and _____, and the second system drives the _____ or _____.

24. ____________________________
    ____
    ____

25. An electric starter uses _____ current which is converted to _____ current for the starter motor.
    a. 110 volt dc, 12 volt ac
    b. 110 volt ac, 12 volt dc
    c. 12 volt dc, 110 volt ac
    d. 12 volt ac, 110 volt dc

25. ____________________________

26. Electric starting requires a 3-wire grounded _____ _____. 26. ____________

27. Identify the parts of the auger gear box illustrated below.

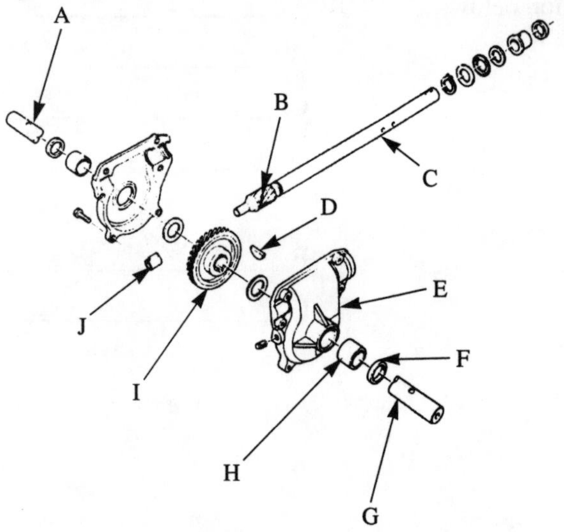

27. A. ____________
B. ____________
C. ____________
D. ____________
E. ____________
F. ____________
G. ____________
H. ____________
I. ____________
J. ____________

28. Self-propelled snow throwers use a(n) _____ _____ mechanism to vary the speed of the machine. 28. ____________

29. On track driven machines it is very important that the track tension be adjusted properly and _____. 29. ____________

30. To remove the drive chain, it is necessary to locate and remove the _____ link and the _____ link. 30. ____________

____

31. To establish the correct height of the auger housing above the ground, adjustment to the _____ _____ is necessary. 31. ____________

32. On smooth surfaces such as concrete or asphalt, the scraper bar should be adjusted to lightly scrape or clear by about _____ or _____. 32. ____________

____

33. On gravel surfaces the scraper bar should be adjusted about _____ about _____. 33. ____________

____

34. The scraper bar adds _____ to the auger housing. 34. ____________

35. On snow throwers with operator presence controls, the auger stops rotating when the _____ _____ is released. 35. ____________

36. The engine should always be _____ and the spark plug wire should be _____ before reaching into the auger housing or chute to clear an obstruction. 36. ____________

____

Name ________________________________

37. Identify the snow thrower controls in the illustration below.

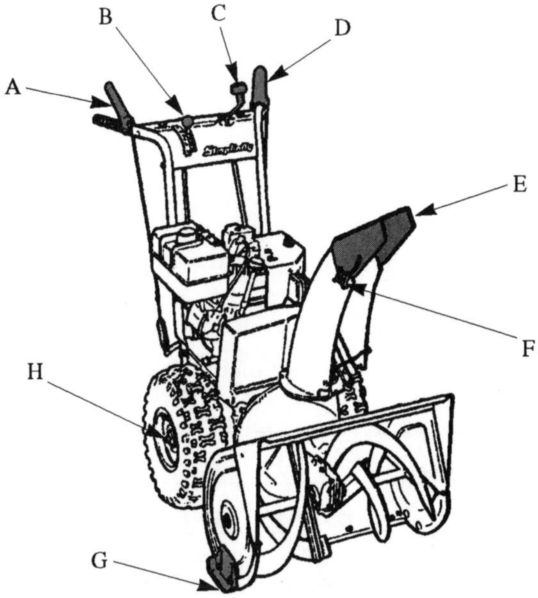

A
B
C
D
E
F
G
H

37. A. ____________________
B. ____________________
C. ____________________
D. ____________________
E. ____________________
F. ____________________
G. ____________________
H. ____________________

38. List the procedure for starting a snow thrower engine. ____________________

____

____

____

____

____

____

____

39. For best performance, a snow thrower engine should be run at _____.

    a. slow speed
    b. medium speed
    c. high speed
    d. Any speed is suitable.

39. ____________________

40. Before removing the fuel tank cap on a snow thrower you should remove any ____________________

____.

41. Water in the fuel will freeze in the _____ part of the system and prevent starting.

41. ____________________

42. It is best to fill the fuel tank after each use of the snow thrower to avoid _____.

42. ____________________

43. The auger gear box must be lubricated with a(n) _____ _____ worm gear oil.

43. ____________________

44. If either, or both, of the auger halves should stop turning even though the auger clutch is engaged, the problem is probably ____

____

____.

45. External mechanical parts of the snow thrower can be lubricated with ____.
    a. 10W oil
    b. molybdenum disulfide grease
    c. lithium grease

45. ______________________

46. Why is it necessary to liberally lubricate the exterior of the solid shafts of the gear box when assembling the auger tubes over them? ____

____

47. How can the auger tubes be lubricated periodically without disassembling them? ______________________

____

48. What are two possible reasons the unit may fail to propel itself? ______________________

____

____

• Research and write complete answers to the following questions.

49. Describe how the friction disc works for changing the speed of the snow thrower wheels. ______________

____

____

____

____

____

____

____

50. Describe how to prepare a snow thrower for off-season storage. ______________________

____

____

____

____

____

____

____

____

____

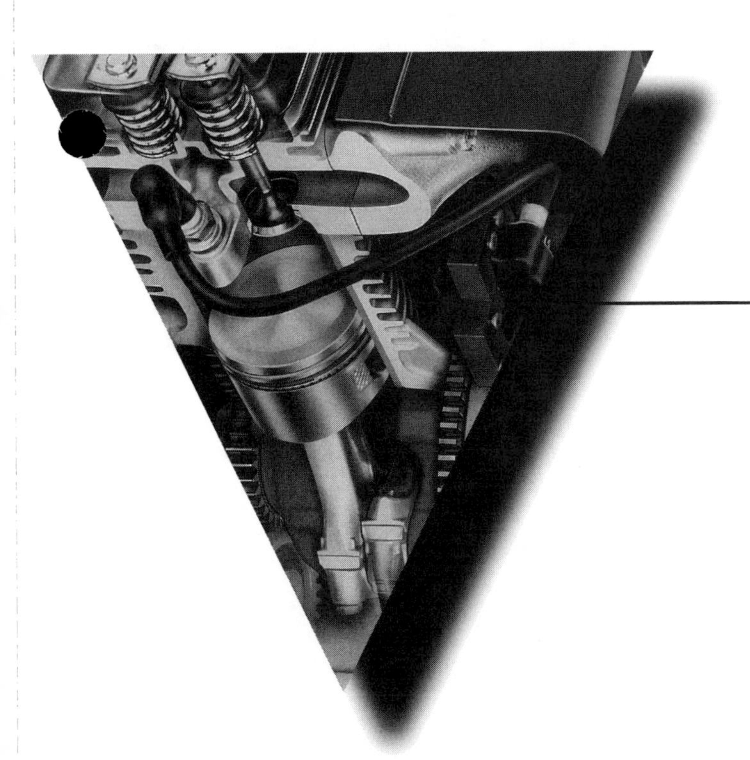

Personal Watercraft

Name_______________

Date _______________ Period _______________

Instructor_______________

After studying this chapter, you will be able to:

▼ Describe personal watercraft safety and established boating regulations.
▼ Understand the major components of personal watercraft.
▼ Explain proper personal watercraft operation.
▼ Understand personal watercraft engine systems.
▼ Maintain and make adjustments to personal watercraft.
▼ Properly store and remove from storage a personal watercraft.

Instructions: After studying Chapter 21 in the text, complete the following questions and problems.

1. Personal watercraft are a type of boat that is propelled by a forceful _____ of _____. 1. _______________ _______________

2. The U.S. Coast Guard considers all personal watercraft, regardless of _____, to be power boats. 2. _______________

3. Class A Inboard Boats are _____ in length. 3. _______________
   a. less than 16 feet
   b. between 20 and 30 feet
   c. between 25 and 35 feet
   d. None of the above.

4. Over _____ of boats in use today are in the Class A category. 4. _______________
   a. 35%
   b. 45%
   c. 55%
   d. 65%

5. State laws regarding PWC are _____.
   a. the same in every state
   b. the same in only twelve states
   c. different in Hawaii and Alaska
   d. required to be known by each PWC owner/operator

5. ______________________

6. PWC are different from most other boats in that they do not have a(n) _____ and _____.

6. ______________________
____

7. The jet of water is propelled by a(n) _____ _____ pump mechanism.

7. ______________________

8. The capabilities and limitations of PWC are somewhat different than other propeller driven boats in that they can operate in _____ water and are more easily _____.

8. ______________________
____

9. Waves, turbulence and obstructions affect PWC _____.
   a. less than other boats
   b. more than other boats
   c. the same as other boats

9. ______________________

10. In boat traffic conditions with a PWC, it is important to take extra _____.

10. ______________________

11. A PWC operator should know all _____ and _____ rules and safe boating practices.

11. ______________________
____

12. Identify the components of the PWC illustrated below.

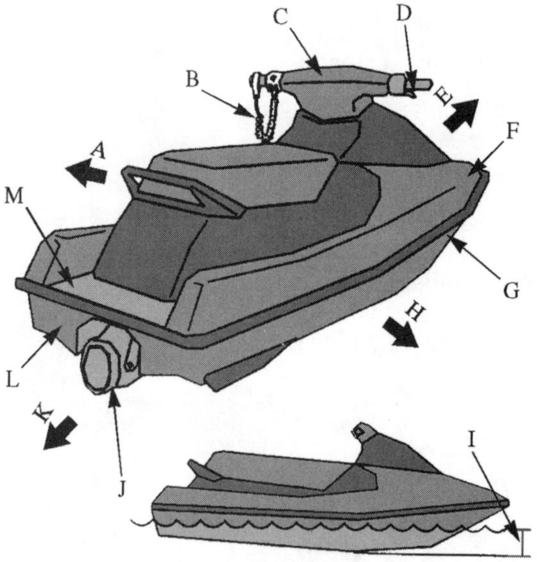

12. A. ______________________
B. ______________________
C. ______________________
D. ______________________
E. ______________________
F. ______________________
G. ______________________
H. ______________________
I. ______________________
J. ______________________
K. ______________________
L. ______________________
M. ______________________

13. It is recommended that all operators complete a boating _____ course.

13. ______________________

14. Statistics show that _____ and lack of _____ are the chief reasons why PWC are involved in accidents.

14. ______________________
____

Name ________________________________

15. The Department of Natural Resources (DNR), PWC manufacturers, boating organizations, and boating law administrators are working to establish _____ for all _____ of PWC.

15. ____________________

____

16. Boating operators over 16 years of age _____.
    a. are required to have some boating education
    b. must have permission from the U.S. Coast Guard
    c. are not required to have any boating education
    d. must have a drivers license to operate a boat

16. ____________________

17. Operators and passengers of PWC should become familiar with PWC _____ _____ before riding.

17. ____________________

18. PWC _____ stop very quickly in the water.
    a. can
    b. cannot

18. ____________________

19. After operating a PWC at full throttle, it will take about _____ to stop.
    a. the length of one football field
    b. 300 yards
    c. 120 feet
    d. 645 feet

19. ____________________

20. Speed limits on the water _____.
    a. are nonexistent
    b. range from 20 to 30 mph
    c. are posted with signs or buoys
    d. None of the above.

20. ____________________

21. The operator and passenger must be wearing a U.S. Coast Guard Approved _____ _____ _____ at all times.

21. ____________________

22. The seat of a PWC _____ designed to be an auxiliary flotation device.
    a. is
    b. is not

22. ____________________

23. List at least three wearing apparel items that the operator of a PWC can wear for personal protection.

____

____

____

____

24. Before starting a PWC, the operator must make sure the _____ is connected to his/her wrist or PFD to prevent being stranded.

24. ____________________

25. A federal regulation requires that an approved operable _____ _____ be on board.

25. ____________________

26. Hypothermia can begin in water as warm as _____ degrees Fahrenheit.

26. ____________________

27. When going into open water or remote areas, it is safest to go with another _____ and to take a(n) _____ _____. 27. ____________________ ____________________

28. Severe injury can take place from the _____ _____ _____ from the jet pump and from falling into the water at high speed. 28. ____________________

29. Explain how the lanyard protects the operator from being stranded after falling from the PWC.

____

____

____

30. The minimum depth of water to ride a PWC in is _____ feet of water. 30. ____________________

31. Why is riding a PWC in shallow water a problem? ____________________

____

____

____

32. Idle speed should not be exceeded in water that is less than ______ feet deep. 32. ____________________

33. If a PWC is capsized (turned over) it must be righted in the direction the manufacturer specifies or water will enter the _____ through the _____ system. 33. ____________________ ____________________

34. Alcohol is involved in over _____ of all boating accidents. 34. ____________________

35. List six items that should be included in a pre-ride outside check.

____

____

____

____

____

____

36. List at least seven items that should be included in the inside check of a PWC.

____

____

____

____

____

____

____

Name ____________________

37. Identify the parts of the fuel sediment bowl in the following illustration.

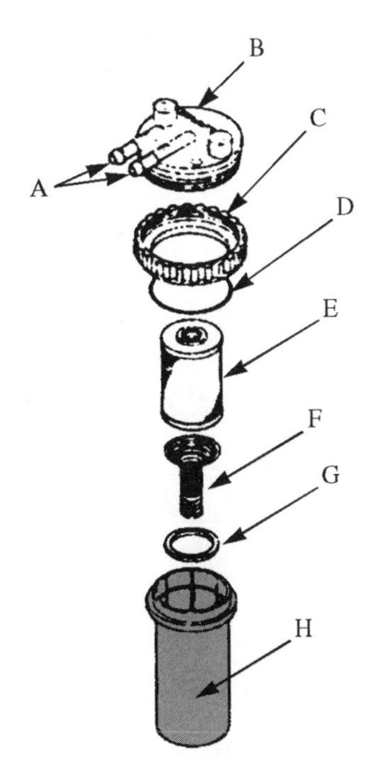

37. A. ____________
B. ____________
C. ____________
D. ____________
E. ____________
F. ____________
G. ____________
H. ____________

38. Why is it important to ventilate the bilge before starting the engine? ____________

____

____

____

39. Since there are so many items that need to be checked, a plastic _____ check list can be extremely useful.

39. ____________

40. Identify the components indicated in the illustration below.

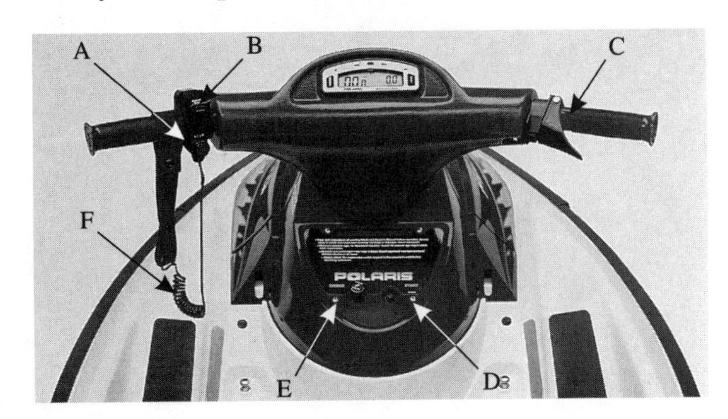

40. A. ____________
B ____________
C. ____________
D. ____________
E. ____________
F. ____________

41. List at least three launch ramp courtesies.

____

____

____

42. Registration numbers must be located visibly on _____.
    a. one side of the hull
    b. one side of the hull and the stern
    c. both sides of the hull
    d. the stern only

42. _______________

43. United States waterways are marked for safe navigation by _____.
    a. signs
    b. symbols and buoys
    c. markers
    d. All of the above.

43. _______________

44. PWC operators are responsible for any damage caused by their craft's _____ .

44. _______________

45. The stand-on vessel _____.
    a. must give way to all other vessels
    b. has the right of way over other vessels
    c. never has to give way to another vessel

45. _______________

46. Carefully draw lines and arrows indicating the proper legal paths for each of the PWC in the following illustrations.

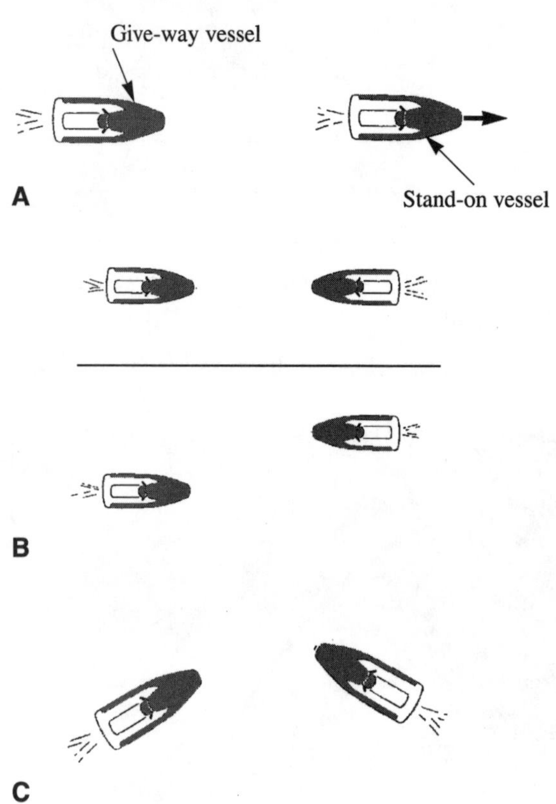

Name ______________________________

47. Identify the main parts of the following PWC illustrations.

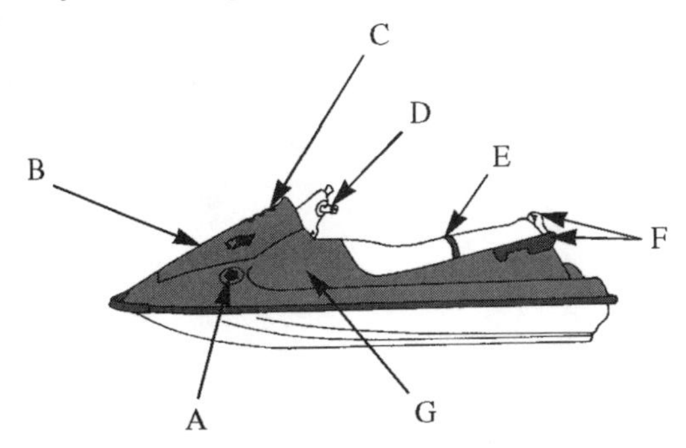

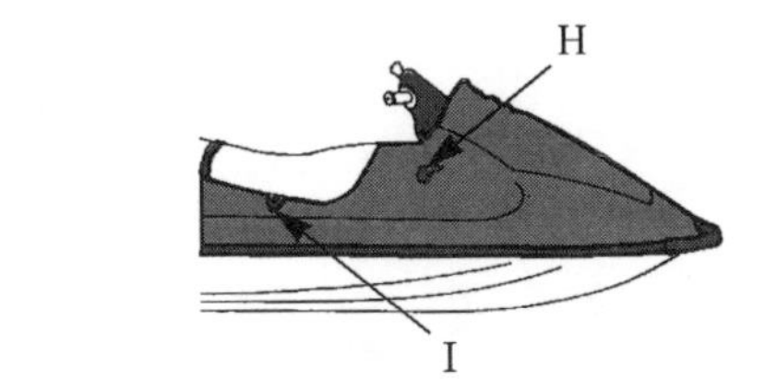

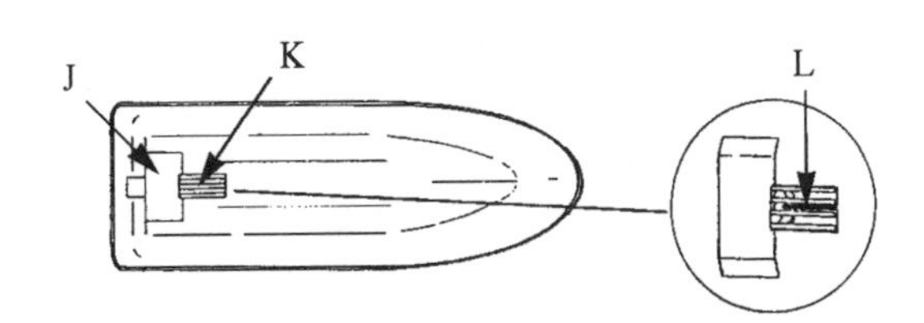

47. A. ____________
B. ____________
C. ____________
D. ____________
E. ____________
F. ____________
G. ____________
H. ____________
I. ____________
J. ____________
K. ____________
L. ____________

48. To avoid serious injury, never let anyone in the water get near the _____ _____ or the intake _____ when the engine is running.

48. ____________

____

49. Engines for PWC are _____ and water-cooled.
   a. all four-cycle
   b. all two-cycle
   c. either two-cycle or four-cycle
   d. two-cycle, four-stroke,

49. ____________

50. The pistons are cast aluminum, alloyed with _____, and _____ or nickel to increase durability and heat resistance.

50. ____________

____

51. To improve the pourability of the molten aluminum for pistons, _____ is added to the alloy.
   a. 10% to 25% silicon
   b. 25% to 45% silicon
   c. 15% to 25% nickel
   d. 20% to 25% lead

51. ____________

52. Why is a pin installed in each of the piston ring grooves? ____________

____

____

53. Identify the parts of the piston in the following illustration.

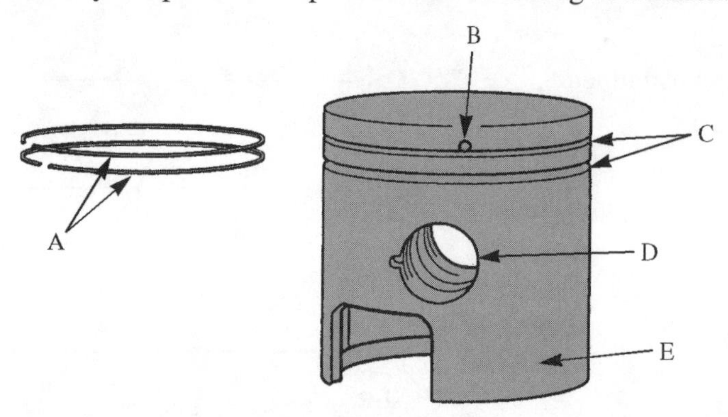

53. A. ____________________
B. ____________________
C. ____________________
D. ____________________
E. ____________________

54. The crankshafts in PWC are assembled as a unit and are supported by _____ _____ mounted inside the _____.

54. ____________________
____

55. Identify the parts of the crankshaft assembly in the following illustration.

55. A. ____________________
B. ____________________
C. ____________________

56. Many PWC use a rotary valve system instead of bypass piston ports. Identify the parts indicated on the following illustration.

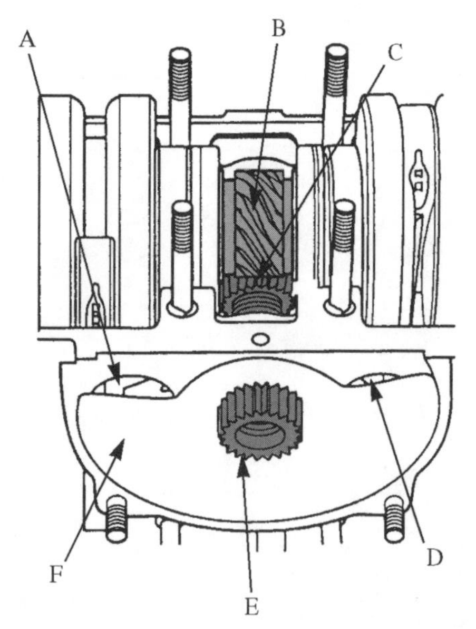

56. A. ____________________
B. ____________________
C. ____________________
D. ____________________
E. ____________________
F. ____________________

Name ______________________________

57. Of the following, the _____ is the most efficient fuel/air intake system.
    a. piston bypass
    b. rotary valve
    c. poppet valve
    d. reed valve

57. ______________________

58. PWC engines are water cooled. The water intake is located in the jet pump and the water is driven in the system by pressure generated in the _____ section.

58. ______________________

59. Performance of a PWC is closely related to the _____ of the impeller blades.

59. ______________________

60. The axial flow jet pump is driven directly from the engine _____.

60. ______________________

61. Steering for PWC is controlled by the hinged _____.

61. ______________________

62. Very close tolerances are maintained between the impeller blades and the _____ ring.

62. ______________________

63. Identify the jet pump parts in the following illustration.

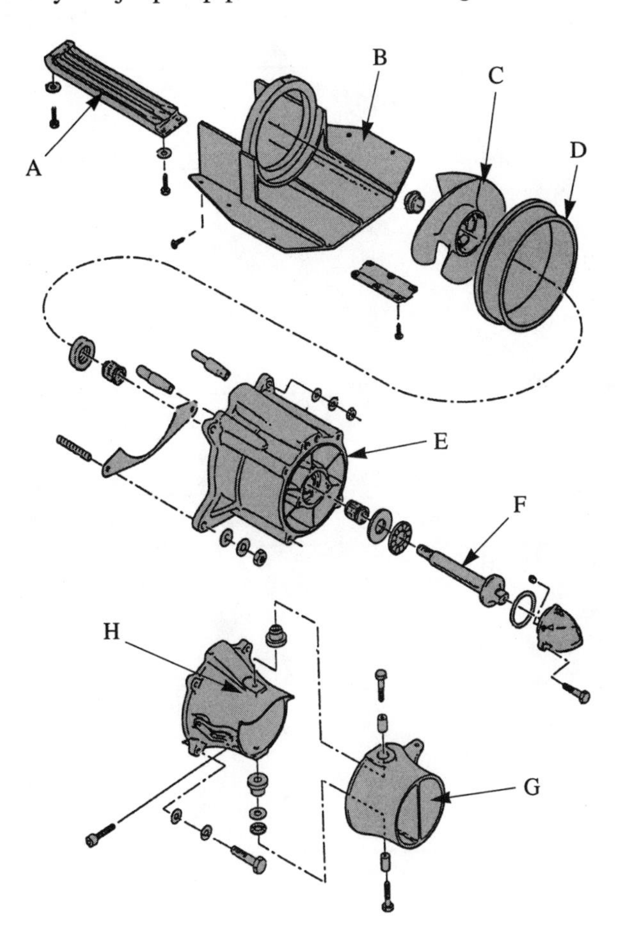

63. A. ______________________
    B. ______________________
    C. ______________________
    D. ______________________
    E. ______________________
    F. ______________________
    G. ______________________
    H. ______________________

64. A new engine needs a careful _____ period. The _____ _____ of the manufacturer's service manual describes the procedure to be used. 64. ____________________ ____________________

65. If extensive engine work is to be done, it will be necessary to obtain some _____ tools from the manufacturer. 65. ____________________

66. The _____ type fuel filter is used in most PWC and is located between the fuel tank and the _____. 66. ____________________ ____________________

67. The fuel vent check valve allows air to _____ the fuel tank but prevents spillage if the PWC is _____. 67. ____________________ ____________________

68. Carburetors for PWC are adjusted at the factory for best _____ _____ conditions. 68. ____________________

69. A PWC engine should never be run without cooling water for more than _____. 69. ____________________
   a. 5 minutes
   b. 15 seconds
   c. 1 minute
   d. 30 seconds

70. The battery in a PWC must be secured in a battery _____ that is fastened securely to the _____. 70. ____________________ ____________________

71. Attempting to charge a frozen battery may cause a(n) _____. 71. ____________________

72. Some PWC have automatic _____ flushing systems. 72. ____________________

73. _____ will cause a PWC engine to overheat and seize causing severe damage. 73. ____________________
   a. Lack of oil in the oil tank
   b. Clogged water inlet in stationary nozzle of pump
   c. Saltwater clogged cooling passages in engine block
   d. Any or all of the above.

74. Transporting a PWC should be done on a trailer with proper _____ and _____ _____ equipment. 74. ____________________ ____________________

75. The trailer for a PWC should be fitted with _____, _____ wheel bearings. 75. ____________________ ____________________

76. If a PWC must be towed to shore, a 20′ (6m) line should be tied to the bow. Towing should not be faster than _____. 76. ____________________
   a. 35 mph
   b. 20 mph
   c. 10 mph
   d. 5 mph

77. List at least four components that should be lubricated when storing a PWC for the season.

____

____

____

____

____

Name ________________________________

78. PWC can be safe and greatly enjoyed if good _____, courtesy toward others, and proper _____ of the PWC is practiced.

78. ______________________

____

• Research and write complete answers to the following questions.

79. Explain how operators of PWC can enjoy the sport and show respect for other boaters with whom they share the water. ____

80. Describe the most important features to consider when purchasing a PWC. ____

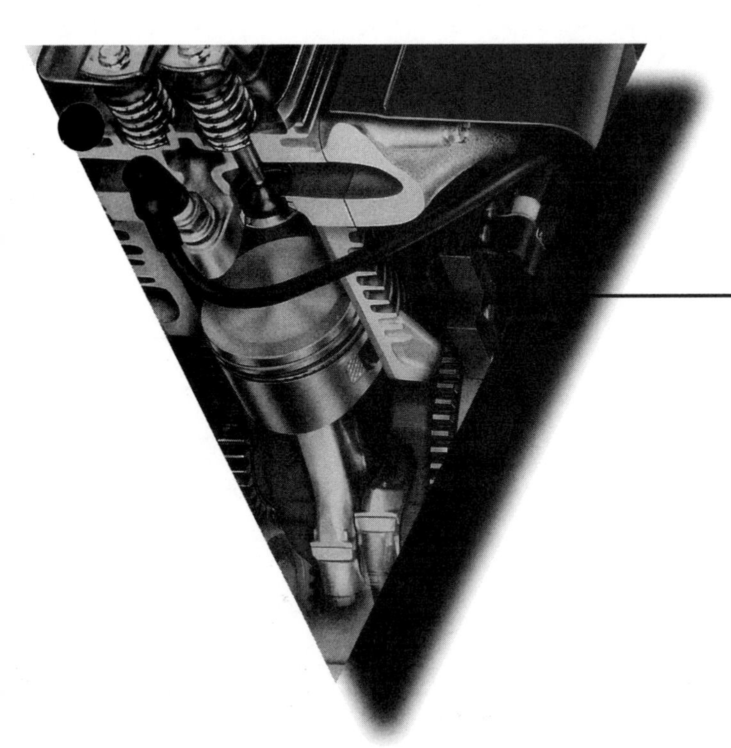

Career Opportunities and Certification

Name________________________________

Date ____________________ Period ____________

Instructor____________________________

After studying this chapter, you will be able to:

- ▼ Identify several career opportunities in the small gas engine field.
- ▼ List qualities that are essential for anyone pursuing a career in small engines.
- ▼ List the advantages and disadvantages of entrepreneurship.
- ▼ Identify the benefits of outdoor power equipment certification.

Instructions: After studying Chapter 22 in the text, complete the following questions and problems.

1. Career opportunities in the small gas engine field exist in three different areas: _____, _____, and _____.
   1. ____________________
   ____
   ____

2. Training, study, and work experience can prepare for employment and careers as the _____ of a small engine service center.
   a. general manager
   b. service technician or manager
   c. sales manager
   d. All of the above.
   2. ____________________

3. The quality of work and reliability of the technician who services a customer's equipment directly affects the _____ and _____ volume of a business.
   3. ____________________
   ____

4. Engine technicians must be able to _____.
   a. diagnose engine problems and make appropriate repairs and/or parts replacement
   b. analyze the mechanical condition and performance of any particular engine and make recommendations to the owner
   c. use test equipment and manufacturers' manuals
   d. All of the above.

4. ____________________

5. Technicians need to know how to use special engine tools and measuring instruments, such as _____, _____, and dial indicators.

5. ____________________
   ____

6. Additional experience in _____ and _____ are desirable.

6. ____________________
   ____

7. The person responsible for writing job tickets, assigning work to the technicians, handling customer inquiries, discussing service problems with customers, and reporting directly to the general manager or owner is the _____ _____.

7. ____________________

8. The _____ location of an implement sales or rental business often determines the type of equipment that is most in demand by the customer.

8. ____________________

9. List four responsibilities required of the general manager of a successful small gas engine and implement business.

____
____
____
____

10. Manufacturers of small gas engines need skilled technicians to help develop _____ engines or new engine _____ and test new design theories.

10. ____________________
    ____

11. Manufacturer's technicians are generally involved with _____ of engine designs in the plant and in the field.
    a. analysis
    b. experiments
    c. tests
    d. All of the above.

11. ____________________

12. Explain why technicians must be able to communicate clearly in technical language with engineers.

____
____
____
____

13. A student can obtain the necessary education to become a technician at _____, _____ _____, and _____.

13. ____________________
    ____
    ____

14. Advancement in the field of engine mechanics and technical training can be obtained by attending _____ _____ and _____ _____ programs.

14. ____________________
    ____

Name ______________________________________

15. Describe some of the responsibilities of the manufacturer's service representative. ____________________
____
____
____
____

16. What kind of training and education is needed to become an engineer? ____________________________
____
____
____
____

17. Many of the executives in the field of outdoor power equipment and engine manufacturing began their careers in _____. 17. ____________________
    a. engine production
    b. design
    c. sales or service
    d. All of the above.

18. People who start their own business in the small engine and outdoor equipment field are called _____. 18. ____________________

19. Explain the advantages of having one's own business. ____________________________________
____
____
____
____

20. What are some of the possible difficulties associated with having one's own business? ________________
____
____
____
____

21. Being a teacher can be a rewarding career choice if one enjoys working with young people. A qualified individual can seek a teaching career in _____ technology, or _____ education. 21. ____________________
____

22. To teach at the high school or vocational school level, a(n) _____ _____ with a specialization in teaching is required. 22. ____________________

23. In addition to hiring certified teachers, many community colleges hire teachers that have extensive _____-_____ experiences. 23. ____________________

24. The voluntary technicians certification tests for outdoor power equipment technicians, mechanics, and service managers is available from the _____ _____ _____ Training Council. 24. ____________________

25. Explain why it is desirable to obtain training certification. ____

____

____

____

26. List the six OPE certification tests available.

____

____

____

____

____

____

27. List the four main categories covered in each of the OPE tests.

____

____

____

____

28. There are ______ questions on each test. 28. ____________________
   a. 50 to 75
   b. 75 to 100
   c. 100 to 150
   d. 150 to 200

29. ESA is the abbreviation for the _____ Association. 29. ____________________

• Research and write a complete answer to the following question.

30. After talking with your teacher and school counselor about the possibilities in the small engine and implement field, recap your conversations and describe how you plan to meet your career goals. ____________________

____

____

____

____

____

____

____

____

____

____

____

____

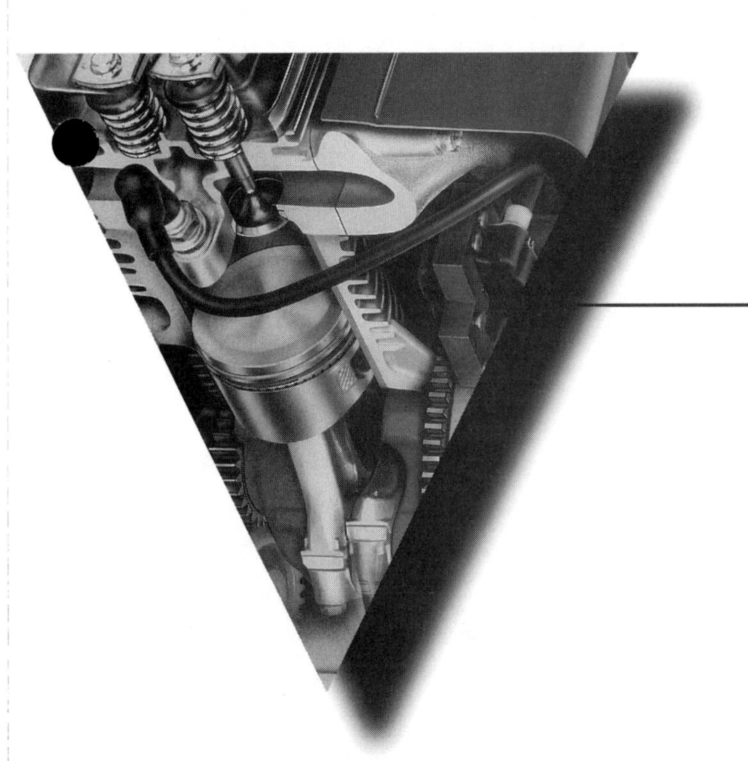

Jobs

The following jobs are designed to supplement the material in the **Small Gas Engines** textbook by outlining various hands-on activities. Before starting any job, read through the entire assignment and discuss the procedure with your instructor. It is also important to read the related chapters in the textbook and review all pertinent safety information before you begin.

Where applicable, references to the **Small Gas Engines Videos** have been placed in the outside margins of the jobs. These references identify sections of the videos that correlate to the job at hand. Each reference contains a letter and a four-digit counter number. The letter identifies the specific video that should be viewed:

- **D** Small Gas Engines—Disassembly
- **I** Small Gas Engines—Inspection, Measurement, Cleaning
- **T** Small Gas Engines—Troubleshooting & Tune-up
- **R** Small Gas Engines—Reassembly

The counter number gives the approximate location (in minutes and seconds) of the pertinent information in the video. Although the videos are not necessary for successful completion of the jobs, they do provide a useful supplement to the material presented in the text.

Some jobs may take more than one class period to complete. If this occurs, be sure to inform your instructor so that your project can be stored properly until you are able to resume work.

As you complete each step in a job, place a check mark in the corresponding box. This will help you keep track of your progress. If any of the steps do not apply to the particular assembly you are working on, mark N/A by the box, for *not applicable.* When you finish an entire job, have your instructor inspect your work and initial your completed job sheet.

MATERIALS AND EQUIPMENT LIST

The following is a list of the materials and equipment that are used or that may be used in the jobs of this workbook. In addition to the tools listed here, other special service tools may be specified in the manufacturer's service manual for the particular vehicle being serviced. Also, replacement parts will be required on an as-needed basis.

Material/Equipment	Job(s)
.50-13 UNC × 2 hex head bolt	5
Air filter cartridge (new)	7, 8
Air filter element	11
Air nozzles	1
Appropriate service manual	3, 4, 6, 7, 8
Bench grinder with wire wheels	6
Brass air gap gauge	7, 8
Breaker points	10
Carburetor cleaning solution and tank	11
Carburetor rebuild kit	11
Chisels	2
Clean shop rags	3, 4, 6, 11
Cleaning brush	6
Cleaning supplies	1
Coil	10
Combination square	6
Combination, box, and open-end wrenches	2, 3, 4, 7, 8, 10, 11

Item	Job
Compressed air	6, 11
Compression tester	9
Condenser	10
Connecting rod bearings (new)	8
Containers and masking tape for storing and labeling small parts	3, 4
Crankcase seals and sealer (new)	7
Crankshaft bore seals and sealer	8
Dial indicator with magnetic base	5
Dial or vernier caliper	6
Electric drill with a rotary brush	6
Engine bench mount	3
Engine that has been in service and preferably indicates some sort of problems	9
Fire extinguishing equipment	1, 7, 8
First aid supplies	1
Flammable waste and liquid storage items	1
Flat metal surface	6
Flat punch	11
Float level gauge or drill bit (proper size)	11
Flywheel key (new)	7, 8
Flywheel puller	3, 4, 10
Four-cycle engine	3
Fuel	7
Fuel filter (new)	7, 8
Fuel line	7, 8
Funnel	2, 3, 4, 11
Gasket adhesive	7
Gasket and carbon removal tool	6
Gasket kit (new)	8
Gasket sealer	8
Grease	7, 8
Hammer	4, 7, 11
Head bolt washers and seals (new, if needed)	7
Ignition tester	10
Machinist's vise with soft jaw covers	2, 5, 7, 8
Metric outside micrometer	5
Motor oil	7, 8
Motor oil container	3
Muffler gasket (new)	7, 8
Ohmmeter	10
Outside micrometers	6
Parts cleaning tank	6
Piston ring expander	3
Piston rings (new)	7, 8
Plastigage	6
Pliers	2, 3, 4, 7, 8, 10, 11
Proper oil/fuel mixture	8
Protective clothing items	1
Ratchet wrench	2, 9
Rebuild gasket kit	7
Reed valve (new)	8
Reed valve O-ring seal or gasket (new)	8
Respirator	11
Retaining ring pliers	7, 8
Ridge reamer	3
Ring expander	7, 8
Ring groove cleaning tool	6
Rubber apron	11
Rubber gloves	11
Ruler (12″)	5
Safety fuel container	2, 3, 4, 11
Safety glasses or goggles	All
Screwdrivers	2, 3, 4, 7, 8, 10, 11
Seal driving tool	7, 8
Service manuals	3, 4, 6, 7, 8
Shallow pans	6
Small chisel (1/7)	11
Small Gas Engines textbook	5
Small hole gauges	5, 6
Small parts containers	6, 11
Socket set	2, 3, 4, 7, 8, 10, 11
Solid-state conversion module	10
Solid-state ignition module	10
Solid-state pulse transformer	10
Spark plug	10
Spark plug socket	2, 3, 4, 9
Spark tester	9
Strap wrench or flywheel tool	7, 8
Surface plate or other flat metal surface	5
Telescoping gauges	5, 6
Thickness gauge	5, 6, 7, 8, 10
Thread pitch gauge	5
Torque wrench	2, 5, 7, 8, 9
Troubleshooting chart	9
Two-cycle engine	4
US customary outside micrometer	5
Valve spring compressor	3, 7
Valve stem caps (for OHV engines)	7
Valve stem grinder	7
Valve stem seals	7
Vee blocks	7
Ventilation equipment	1
Wire brush	6
Wood blocks	7

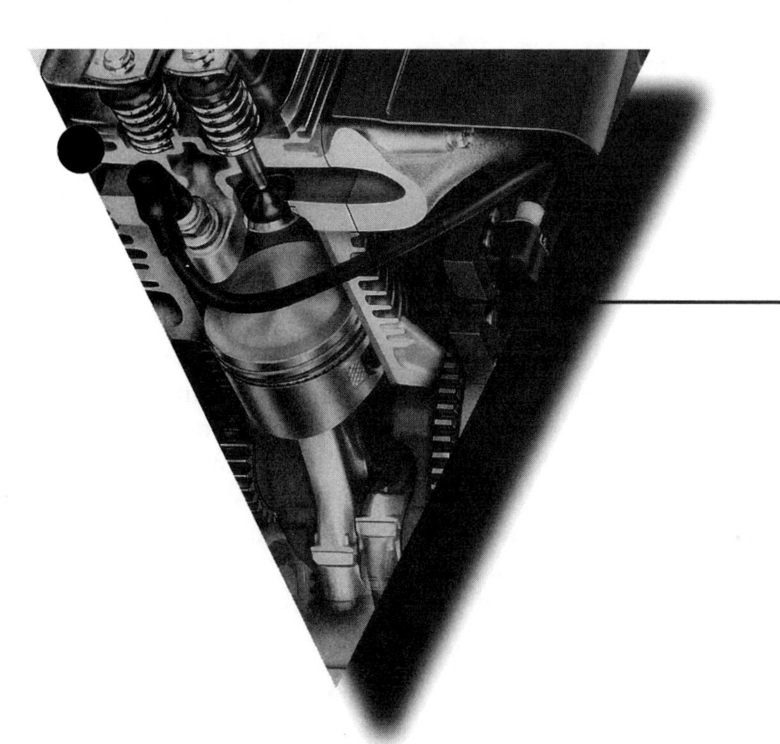

JOB 1

Shop Safety

Name ______________________________

Date ____________________ Score________

Instructor ____________________________

Introduction

A safe shop is well organized and well maintained. Serious injuries can occur when a careless action takes place. It is everyone's job to work carefully and to see that the workplace is safe for all. A safe work attitude should become part of the technician's daily routine.

Objective

After successfully completing this job, you will be able to locate the fire extinguishers, safety glasses, and other safety equipment in your shop. You will understand the general safety rules that must be followed in the small engine shop.

Materials and Equipment

To complete this job, you will need the following materials and equipment:

- Safety glasses or goggles
- Protective clothing items
- Fire extinguishing equipment
- Flammable waste and liquid storage items
- Air nozzles
- Ventilation equipment
- Cleaning supplies
- First aid supplies

Instructions

Before beginning this job, study Chapter 1 in the **Small Gas Engines** textbook, *Safety in the Small Gas Engine Shop.* As you read the job procedures, perform the tasks and answer all questions. As you complete each numbered step, place a check mark in the corresponding box. This will help you keep track of your progress. When you finish the job, ask your instructor to inspect your work and initial your completed job sheet.

Before performing this job, review all pertinent safety information in the text and discuss safety procedures with your instructor.

Procedure

Eye Safety

1. Eye protection (safety glasses or goggles) should be worn during any activity that may cause injury to the eyes. See **Figure 1-1.** The best practice is to wear OSHA-approved safety glasses at all times in the small engine shop. Eye protection should also be worn outdoors when servicing or operating any kind of mechanical equipment. Examples of activities that have the potential to cause injury to eyes include drilling, grinding, hammering, sandblasting, using compressed air, splashing of injurious fluids, and working around a running engine or its accessories. Once you establish the habit of wearing safety glasses on the job, you will feel uneasy about not having them. Should you forget your safety glasses, leave the work area until you can obtain proper eye protection.

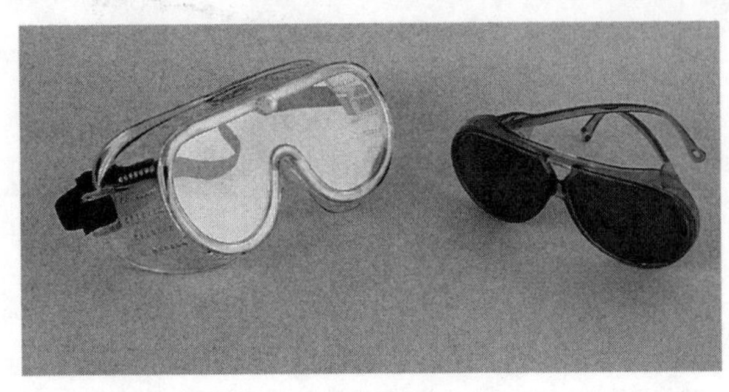

Figure 1-1. *OSHA-approved safety glasses or goggles should always be worn in the small engine shop.*

What is the policy regarding safety glasses and goggles in your shop? ________

____

____ Completed ❑

2. Where are the safety glasses and goggles located? ________________________

____

____ Completed ❑

Safe Clothing

3. What kind of clothing should be worn when working on an engine or an implement?

____

____ Completed ❑

4. Where is the protective clothing, such as work gloves, aprons, welding gloves, goggles, filter masks, etc., located in your shop facility? ________________

____

____ Completed ❑

Name ______________________________

Fire Prevention and Control

5. Locate all the fire extinguishers, fire blankets, fire exits, and fire alarms in your shop. Read the fire evacuation procedure posted in the shop. Completed ❑
6. How many fire extinguishers are there in the shop? ______________ Completed ❑
7. What types of fire extinguishers are found in the shop? ______________

   ______________________________ Completed ❑
8. On what types of fires can these extinguishers be used? See **Figure 1-2.**

   ____

   ______________________________ Completed ❑

Fires	*Type*	*Use*	*Operation*
A **Class A fires** Ordinary combustible materials such as wood, paper, textiles and so forth. Requires... cooling–quenching.	**Soda–acid** Bicarbonate of soda solution and sulfuric acid.	OK for A; Not for B C	Soda–acid: Direct stream at base of flame.
	Pressurized Water Water under pressure.	OK for A; Not for B C	Pressurized water: Direct stream at base of flame.
B **Class B fires** Flammable liquids, greases, gasoline, oils, paints, and so forth. Requires... blanketing or smothering.	**Carbon Dioxide** Carbon dioxide gas under pressure.	Not for A; OK for B C	Carbon dioxide: Direct discharge as close to fire as possible. First at edge of flames and gradually forward and upward.
	Foam Solution of aluminum sulfate and bicarbonate of soda.	OK for A B; Not for C	Foam: Direct stream into the burning material or liquid. Allow foam to fall lightly on fire.
C **Class C fires** Electrical equipment, motors, switches, and so forth. Requires... a nonconducting agent.	**Dry Chemical**	Multi-purpose type: OK for A B C; Ordinary BC type: Not for A, OK for B C	Dry chemical: Direct stream at base of flames, use rapid left-to-right motion toward flames.

Figure 1-2. *Fire extinguisher types and fire classifications. An extinguisher designed to suppress electrical and chemical fires should be used in the small engine shop.*

9. Where are the fire alarms located? ______________________________

____

______________________________ Completed ❑

10. Where and how is gasoline stored? ______________________________

______________________________ Completed ❑

11. Where are the flammable wastes stored? ______________________________

______________________________ Completed ❑

12. Where are oils and other flammable liquids kept? ______________________________

______________________________ Completed ❑

13. Where is the parts cleaning tank? ______________________________ Completed ❑

14. Does the parts cleaning tank have a fusible link-supported lid? What is the purpose of a fusible link? ______________________________

____

______________________________ Completed ❑

Ventilation

15. A properly designed ventilation system should be installed in the small gas engine shop to remove the poisonous exhaust gasses produced by running engines. Never rely on open doors or windows to vent gases.

Where is the switch used to control the ventilation system in your shop?

____

______________________________ Completed ❑

Compressed Air

16. Compressed air is often used to clean and dry parts. Compressed air in hoses and lines may exceed 100 psi (689 kPa). This air pressure can be very dangerous if used carelessly. Only use OSHA-approved air nozzles. These nozzles are designed to dissipate the air pressure as it leaves the nozzle. Never point an air nozzle at your body or at any other individual. Compressed air should never be used to clean clothing or to blow dirt off workbenches.

Shut off the compressed air system and check the condition of the hoses. Also, make sure all connections are tight. List any problems that you find. __________

____

____

______________________________ Completed ❑

Work Area Safety

17. Is the shop clean and well organized? ______________________________ Completed ❑

18. Locate brooms, dustpans, rags, sinks, soap, towels, and waste receptacles. Are these items conveniently located? ______________________________ Completed ❑

Name ________________________________

19. Locate the tools you will need to work on engines. Are the tools clean, neatly organized, and easy to obtain? ________________________________

____

____ Completed ☐

20. Locate specialized test equipment that will be needed. Is it well organized and in good condition? ________________________________

____

____ Completed ☐

21. Are work benches clean and is there adequate space to work safely? ________

____ Completed ☐

22. Is there adequate room between workstations to avoid colliding with others?

____ Completed ☐

23. Is the first aid kit in a prominent location? ____________________

____ Completed ☐

24. Is the first aid kit properly stocked? ________________________

____ Completed ☐

25. Can you suggest any safety improvements to the shop? ______________

____

____ Completed ☐

Instructor's Initials ____________________

Date ____________________

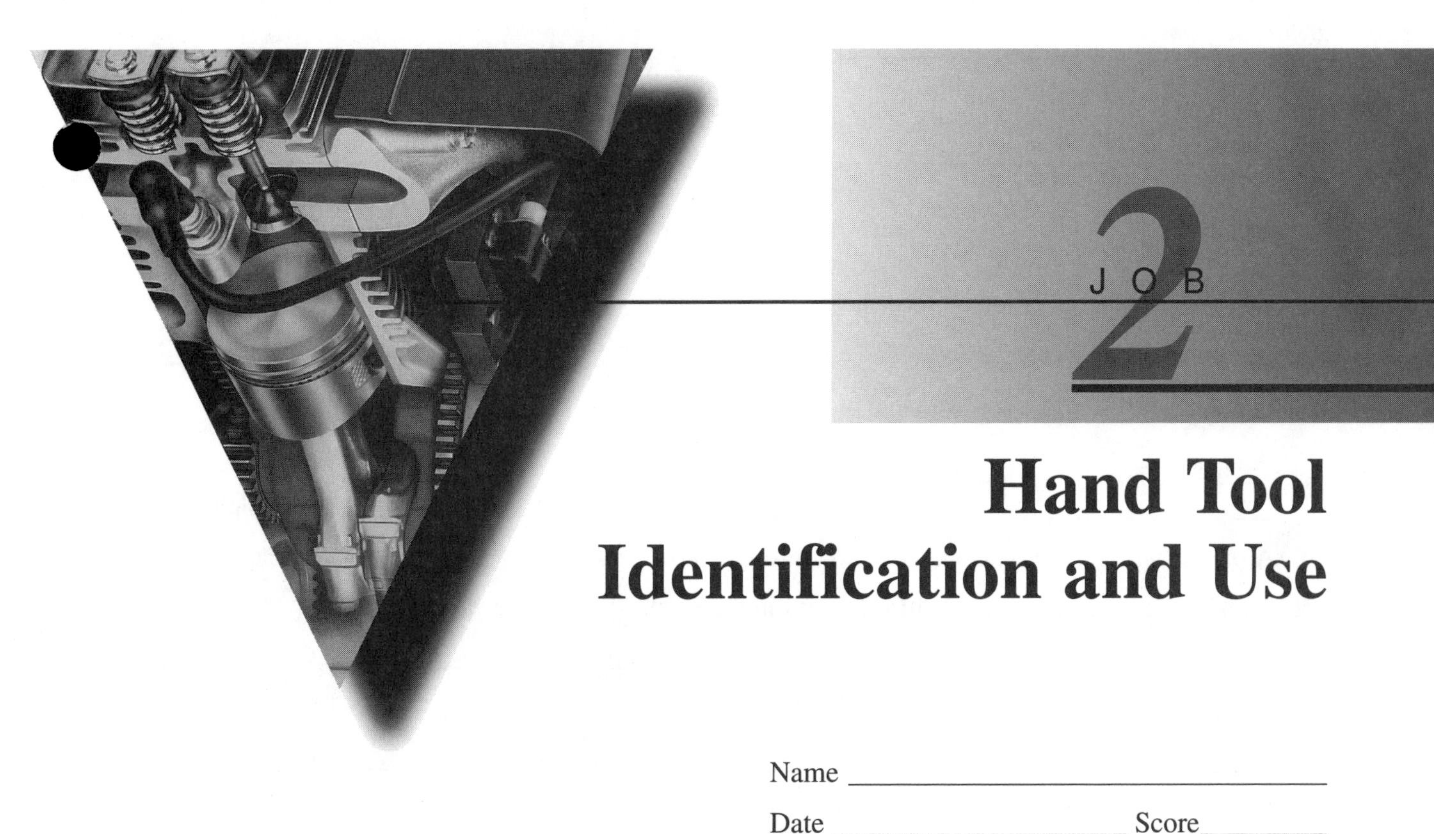

Hand Tool Identification and Use

Name ______________________________

Date ____________________ Score________

Instructor ___________________________

Introduction

Hand tools are used to disassemble, repair, and reassemble small gas engines. Some tools are quite common; others are designed for specific purposes. Tools are extensions of the technician's arms and hands. The small engine technician's skill and experience is evident in the way he or she uses tools to repair and service engines and related implements.

Objective

After successfully completing this job, you will be able to identify and use many of the tools commonly used in the shop to disassemble and assemble an engine.

Materials and Equipment

To complete this job, you will need the following materials and equipment:

- Chisels
- Combination, box, and open-end wrenches
- Funnel
- Machinist's vise
- Pliers
- Ratchet wrench
- Safety fuel container
- Screwdrivers
- Sockets
- Spark plug socket
- Torque wrench

Instructions

After reading Chapter 2, *Tools and Measuring Instruments,* in the **Small Gas Engines** textbook, complete the activities specified in this job. As you read the job procedure, perform the tasks and answer all questions. As you complete each numbered step, place a check mark in the corresponding box. This will help you keep track of your progress. When you finish the job, ask your instructor to inspect your work and initial your completed job sheet.

Before performing this job, review all pertinent safety information in the text and discuss safety procedures with your instructor.

Procedure

1. Where are the tools stored in your shop? ______________________ Completed ❑
2. Are the shop tools clean and in good condition? ______________________ Completed ❑
3. List the types of wrenches available in the shop. ______________________
____
____ Completed ❑
4. Are these wrenches available in both US customary and metric sizes? __________ Completed ❑
5. Look at the heads of the cold chisels found in the shop. Are they mushroomed?
____ Completed ❑
6. Why is a mushroomed head on a cold chisel dangerous?______________________
____ Completed ❑
7. Locate the machinist's vise in your shop. Are soft jaw covers available for use when working with delicate parts? _____ What materials can be used to pad the vise jaws when soft covers are not available?______________________ Completed ❑

You will need an engine and a workstation to complete steps 8-16. The type of engine used will determine tools needed for each step. It will be helpful to review the **Small Gas Engines—Inspection, Measurement, Cleaning** video and the **Small Gas Engines—Disassembly** video, which are available from Goodheart-Willcox Publisher.

8. Remove the spark plug with a ratchet wrench and a spark plug socket. Set the plug aside. What size socket was used to remove the plug? ______________ Completed ❑
9. With the engine resting on the shop floor, shut off the fuel valve and remove the fuel lines. If there is no fuel valve, the tank must be emptied before the lines can be removed. Neoprene fuel lines can be removed with a pair of combination slip joint pliers. Completed ❑
10. Remove the fuel tank. Empty any fuel from the tank. Be careful not to spill the fuel. Pour the fuel into an appropriate container. What tools were used to remove the fuel tank? ______________________________
____ Completed ❑
11. Remove the air cleaner. List the tools needed to remove the air cleaner. ______
____ Completed ❑
12. Remove the muffler. List the tools needed to accomplish this task.__________
____ Completed ❑

Name ________________________________

13. Remove the shroud cover and the starter mechanism from over the flywheel. Usually, a Phillips screwdriver and a socket wrench are needed. Completed ❑
14. Reinstall each part removed from the engine. Use a torque wrench and a spark plug socket to install the spark plug. Torque the spark plug to 13 ft-lb. Completed ❑
15. Clean and replace the tools you have used. Completed ❑
16. Clean your work area. Completed ❑

Instructor's Initials ______________________

Date ____________________________

Four-Cycle Engine Disassembly

Name ___________________________________

Date _____________________ Score_________

Instructor ________________________________

Introduction

It is often necessary to disassemble a small gas engine during repair procedures. Disassembly will expose all the internal engine parts and permit analysis of their condition.

In this job, you will disassemble a four-cycle engine. It may be an engine that is on a used implement or one that is quite clean and used only for instructional purposes. If the engine is mounted on an implement, such as a lawnmower, it must be removed.

Either a valve-in-block engine or an overhead valve engine can be used for this job. Additionally, the engine can have a vertical shaft or a horizontal shaft. Some variations in the disassembly procedure will occur with each of these engine types. It is important that you work in a methodical and well-organized way to produce optimum results. Make sure that your work area is clean.

Objective

After successfully completing this job, you will be able to properly disassemble a small four-cycle engine.

Materials and Equipment

To complete this job, you will need the following materials and equipment:

- Appropriate service manual
- Combination, box, and open-end wrenches
- Clean shop rags
- Containers and tape for storing and labeling small parts
- Engine bench mount
- Flywheel puller (appropriate for engine type)
- Four-cycle engine
- Funnel
- Motor oil container
- Spark plug socket
- Piston ring expander
- Pliers
- Ridge reamer
- Safety fuel container
- Screwdrivers
- Socket wrench set
- Valve spring compressor

Instructions

Before starting this job, study Chapter 15—*Engine Inspection, Disassembly, and Cylinder Reconditioning*—in your **Small Gas Engines** textbook.

As you read the job procedures, perform the tasks and answer all questions. As you complete each numbered step, place a check mark in the corresponding box. This will help you keep track of your progress. You may follow the check list for disassembly of a 4-cycle engine in the Appendix of the **Small Gas Engines** textbook. You may also follow the procedure outlined in the **Small Gas Engines—Disassembly** video, which is available from Goodheart-Willcox Publisher. When you finish this job, ask your instructor to inspect your work and initial your completed job sheet.

Before performing this job, review all pertinent safety information in the text and discuss safety procedures with your instructor.

Procedure

D—0150

Inspection

1. Inspect the engine for signs of trouble before removing it from the implement. Check for oil leaks, fuel leaks, loose or broken engine mounts, misaligned pulleys, and unevenly worn drive belts. Completed ❑

D—0435

External Parts

Keep the parts organized as you remove them from the engine. Do not pile parts on top of each other. Clean tin cans or similar containers are useful for storing small parts. Masking tape labels can be applied to the containers to identify the parts.

2. Remove the spark plug and set it aside. Completed ❑
3. If the engine is on an implement, such as a lawnmower, remove any cables or wires preventing engine removal. Completed ❑
4. Shut off the fuel valve. Completed ❑
5. If the engine is on a lawnmower, remove the blade. Completed ❑
6. Remove the engine from the implement. Completed ❑
7. Remove the fuel line. Completed ❑
8. Remove the fuel tank and empty any fuel into an appropriate safety container. Completed ❑
9. Clamp or bolt the engine to an engine bench mount. Completed ❑
10. Drain the oil from the crankcase. Completed ❑
11. Make a diagram of all carburetor linkages to ease reassembly. Remove the carburetor and set it aside. Completed ❑
12. Remove the muffler. Completed ❑

Name ______________________________________

Flywheel

D—0845

13. Remove the flywheel cover, the screen shield, and the recoil starter, **Figure 3-1.** Completed ❑

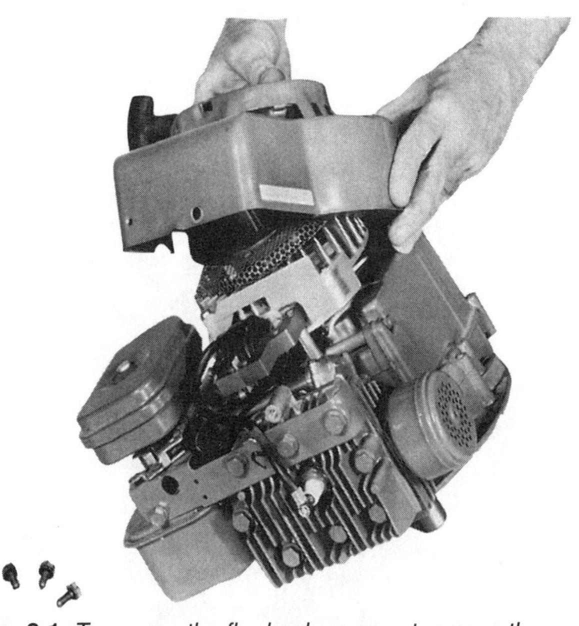

Figure 3-1. *To access the flywheel, you must remove the flywheel cover, the screen shield, and the recoil starter.*

14. Remove the magneto if it is exposed. Otherwise, remove the flywheel; then remove the magneto. Completed ❑
15. Remove the ignition components (solid-state ignition components or the condenser and breaker points). Refer to the service manual for the detailed removal procedure. Disconnect the stop switch wire. Completed ❑
16. Remove the pulley or any other device on the PTO (power take off) end of the crankshaft, if necessary. Completed ❑

Valve Train, Cylinder Head

D—1255

Valve-in-Block Engine

17. Remove the cylinder head. Completed ❑
18. Remove the valve cover. Completed ❑
19. Remove the valve springs and keepers. Completed ❑
20. Remove the valves. Completed ❑

Overhead Valve Engine

21. Remove the valve cover. Completed ❑
22. Remove the rocker arms. Completed ❑
23. Remove the pushrods. Completed ❑
24. Remove the valve springs and keepers. Completed ❑
25. Remove the cylinder head. Completed ❑
26. Remove the valves. Completed ❑

27. After removing the cylinder head, examine the upper edge of the cylinder for a ridge caused by cylinder wear. If there is a ridge, it must be removed with a ridge reamer before removing the piston and rings. Ream only until the ridge is flush with the cylinder wall. Remove any cuttings before attempting to remove the piston. Completed ❑

Internal Parts

D—1450

28. Remove the crankcase cover. Completed ❑
29. Remove the tappets and the camshaft. Completed ❑
30. Remove the rod cap. Completed ❑
31. Rotate the crankshaft to push the piston and connecting rod up in the cylinder. Reverse the crankshaft to disconnect the rod from the crank journal. Completed ❑
32. Remove the piston and connecting rod. See Figure 3-2. Completed ❑

Figure 3-2. *In an integral cylinder block, the piston can be removed through the top of the cylinder. If necessary, use a ridge reaming tool to remove the ridge around the top of the cylinder.*

33. Remove the piston rings with a ring expander tool. Completed ❑
34. Remove the piston pin to disconnect the piston and connecting rod. Completed ❑
35. Remove the crankshaft. Completed ❑
36. Remove the main crankshaft bore seals from the crankcase. Completed ❑

Instructor's Initials ______________________

Date ______________________

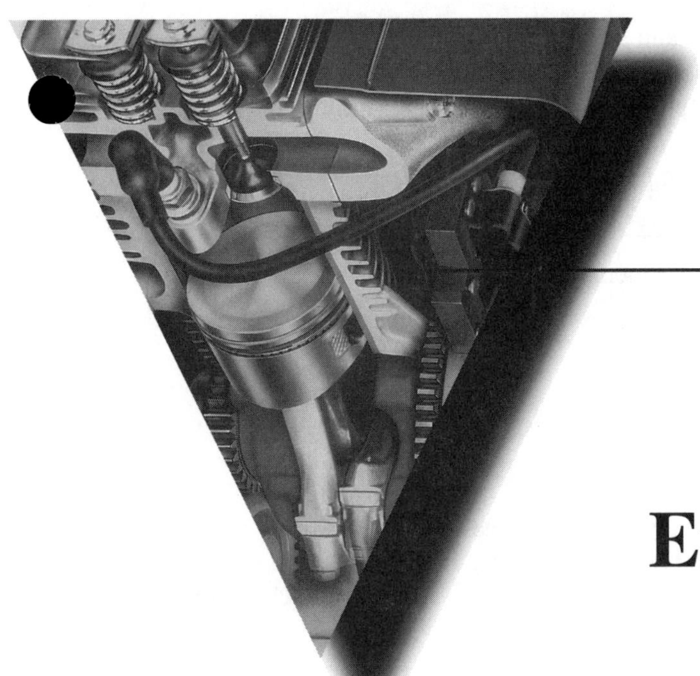

Two-Cycle Engine Disassembly

Name ______________________________

Date ____________________ Score________

Instructor ___________________________

Introduction

In this job, you will disassemble a two-cycle engine. If the engine is mounted on an implement, such as a lawnmower, it must be removed. It is important that you work in a methodical and well-organized way to produce optimum results.

Objective

After successfully completing this job, you will be able to properly disassemble a two-cycle engine.

Materials and Equipment

To complete this job, you will need the following materials and equipment:

- Two-cycle engine
- Appropriate service manual
- Containers and masking tape for storing and labeling small parts
- Clean shop rags
- Socket wrench set
- Spark plug socket
- Combination, box, and open-end wrenches
- Pliers
- Screwdrivers
- Soft-faced hammer
- Safety fuel container
- Funnel
- Flywheel puller (appropriate for engine type)

Instructions

Before starting this job, study Chapter 15—*Engine Inspection, Disassembly, and Cylinder Reconditioning*—in your **Small Gas Engines** textbook.

As you read the job procedures, perform the tasks and answer all questions. As you complete each numbered step, place a check mark in the corresponding box. This will help you keep track of your progress. If desired, you may follow the disassembly procedure outlined in the **Small Gas Engines—Disassembly** video, which is available from Goodheart-Willcox Publisher. When you finish the job, ask your instructor to inspect your work and initial your completed job sheet.

Before performing this job, review all pertinent safety information in the text and discuss safety procedures with your instructor.

Procedure

Inspection

D—0150

1. Inspect the engine for signs of trouble before removing it from the implement. Check for oil leaks, fuel leaks, loose or broken engine mounts, misaligned pulleys, and unevenly worn drive belts. Completed ❑

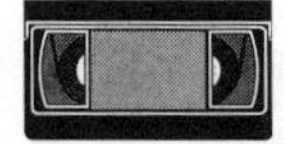

External Parts

D—0435

Keep the parts organized as you remove them from the engine. Coffee cans or similar containers can be used to store small parts. Labels identifying the parts can be applied to the containers.

---

2. Remove spark plug and set it aside. Completed ❑
3. If the engine is on an implement, such as a lawnmower, remove any cables or wires. Completed ❑
4. Shut off the fuel valve. Completed ❑
5. If the engine is on a lawnmower, remove the blade. Completed ❑
6. Remove the engine from the implement. Completed ❑
7. Disconnect and remove the fuel line. Completed ❑
8. Remove the fuel tank and empty any fuel into an appropriate safety container. Completed ❑

Flywheel

D—0855

9. Remove the flywheel cover, the screen shield, and the recoil starter. Completed ❑
10. Remove the ignition points (and condenser) or the ignition module. Completed ❑
11. Use an appropriate flywheel puller to remove the flywheel, **Figure 4-1**. Completed ❑

Figure 4-1. *To prevent flywheel damage, always use an appropriate puller during flywheel removal. (Kubota Tractor Corp.)*

12. Remove the air cleaner assembly. Completed ❑
13. Make a diagram of all carburetor linkage to ease reassembly. Completed ❑
14. Remove the carburetor and set it aside. Completed ❑
15. Remove the blower housing base. Completed ❑
16. Remove the reed valve cover and the reed assembly. Completed ❑
17. Remove the muffler Completed ❑

Internal Parts

D—1450

18. Remove the cylinder from the crankcase. When removing the cylinder, the piston and rings will slide out the bottom of the cylinder. Pull off the cylinder squarely to prevent connecting rod damage. See **Figure 4-2**. Completed ❑

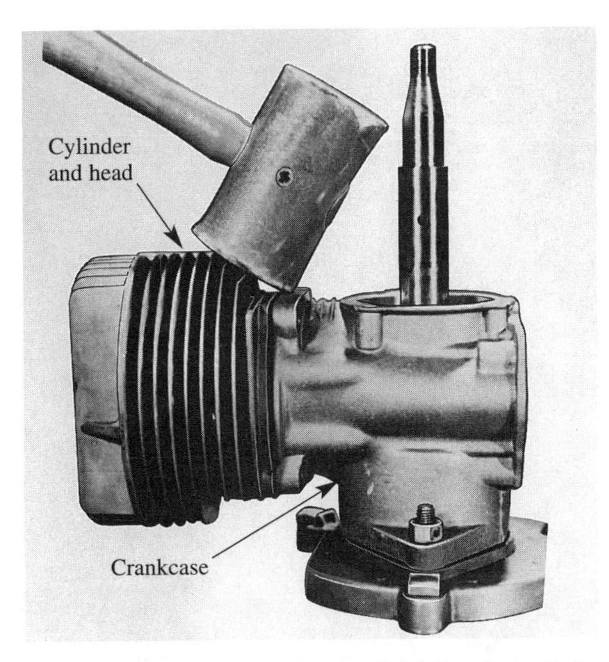

Figure 4-2. *To facilitate cylinder removal, lightly tap the cylinder with a soft-faced hammer. (Lawn-Boy Power Equipment, Gale Products)*

19. Install seal protectors over the ends of the crankshaft.
20. Remove crankcase cover. Do not damage the oil seal when removing the cover. Completed ❑
21. Turn the crankshaft to the top dead center position. Slide the connecting rod off the crank pin and over the crank arm while slowly pulling the crankshaft out through the crankcase cover opening. Completed ❑
22. Remove the piston rings from the piston with a ring expander tool. Completed ❑
23. Remove the piston pin to disconnect the piston and connecting rod. Completed ❑
24. Remove the main crankshaft bore seals from the crankcase. Completed ❑

Instructor's Initials ________________________

Date ________________________

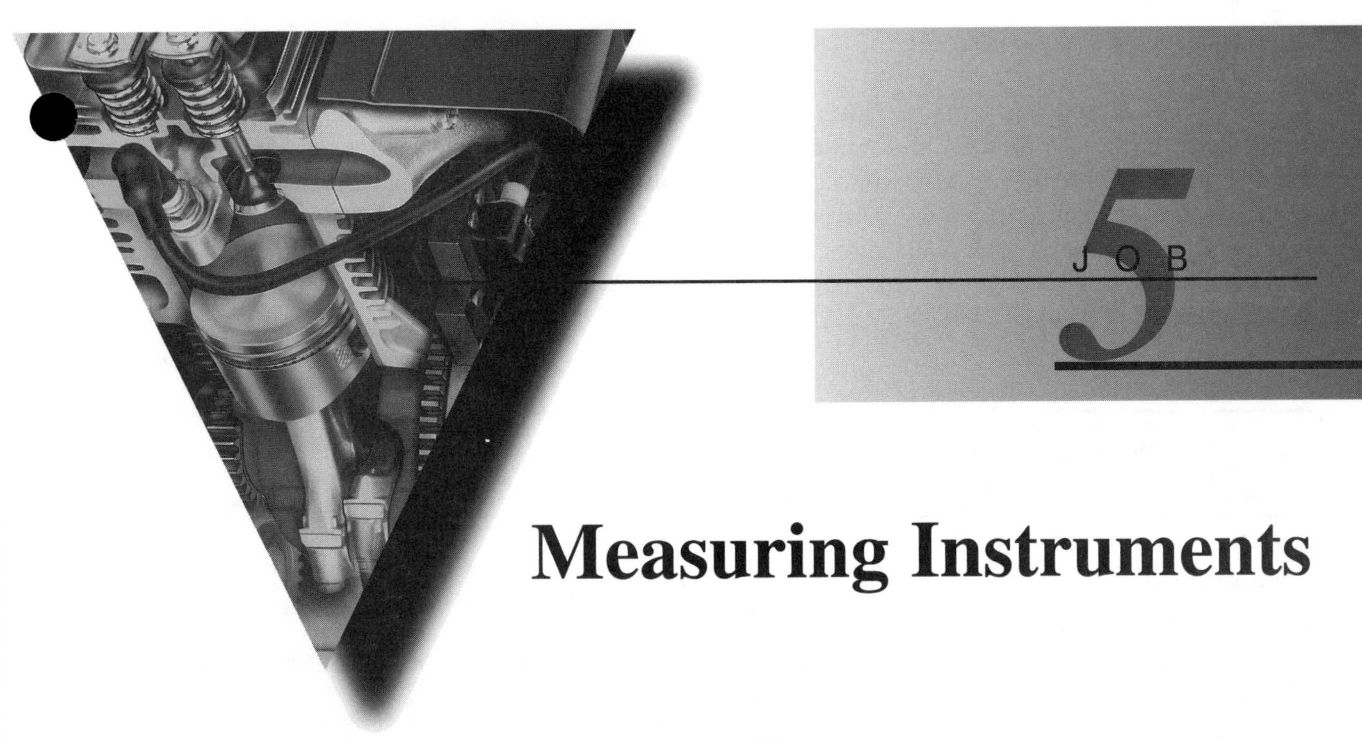

Measuring Instruments

Name ____________________________

Date ____________________ Score__________

Instructor ____________________________

Introduction

Small gas engine technicians rely on measuring instruments to determine whether engine parts are worn beyond tolerable limits. Because parts vary in shape and size, the ability to measure with various kinds of instruments is very important. Engine manuals provide information about basic sizes and acceptable limits for each critical part of an engine. Dimensions may be given in US customary units or in metric units.

Objective

After successfully completing this job, you will be familiar with the measuring instruments needed to determine the condition of various small gas engine parts.

Materials and Equipment

To complete this job, you will need the following materials and equipment:

- 12″ ruler
- Telescoping gauges
- Small hole gauges
- Thickness gauge
- US customary outside micrometer
- Metric outside micrometer
- Dial indicator with magnetic base
- Surface plate or other flat metal surface
- Thread pitch gauge
- Torque wrench with 3/4″ socket
- Machinist's vise with soft jaw covers
- .50-13 UNC × 2 hex head bolt

Instructions

Before attempting this Job, read Chapter 2, *Tools and Measuring Instruments,* in your **Small Gas Engines** textbook. The **Small Gas Engines—Inspection, Measurement, Cleaning** video, available from Goodheart-Willcox Publisher, will show how measuring tools are used to measure engine parts.

As you read the job procedures, perform the tasks and answer all questions. As you complete each numbered step, place a check mark in the corresponding box. This will help you keep track of your progress. When you finish the job, ask your instructor to inspect your work and initial your completed job sheet.

Before performing this job, review all pertinent safety information in the text and discuss safety procedures with your instructor.

Procedures

1. Use a ruler to measure each of the following lines. Write your answer in the blank next to each line. If you need help getting started, ask your instructor for assistance.

_____ a.

_____ b.

_____ c.

_____ d.

_____ e.

_____ f.

_____ g.

_____ h.

_____ i.

_____ j.

Completed ❑

Name ___________________________

2. Measure the following parts with your ruler. Place your answers on the lines provided. Measure the parts, not the dimension lines. Be sure to include units of measure in your answers.

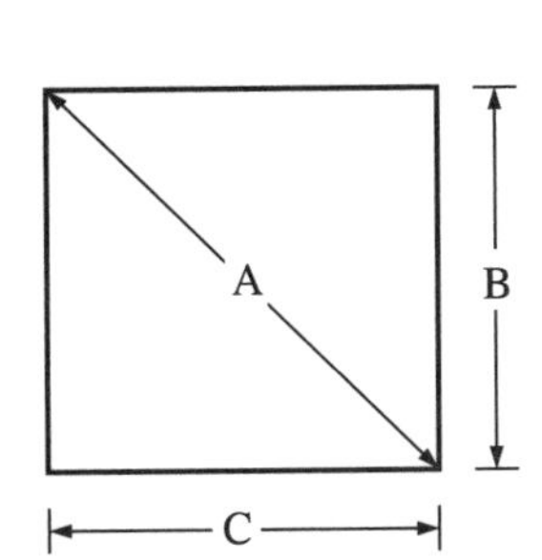

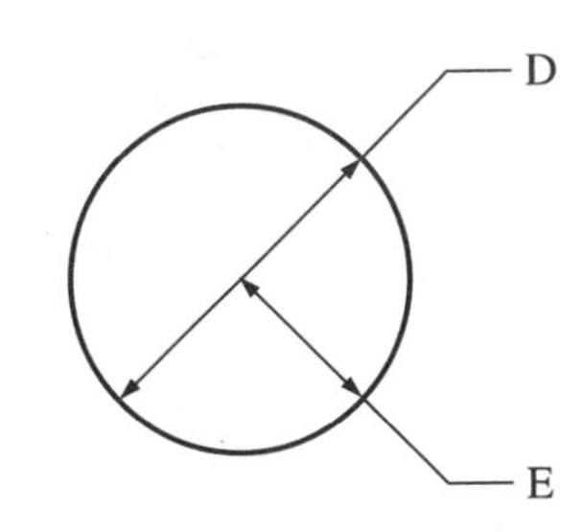

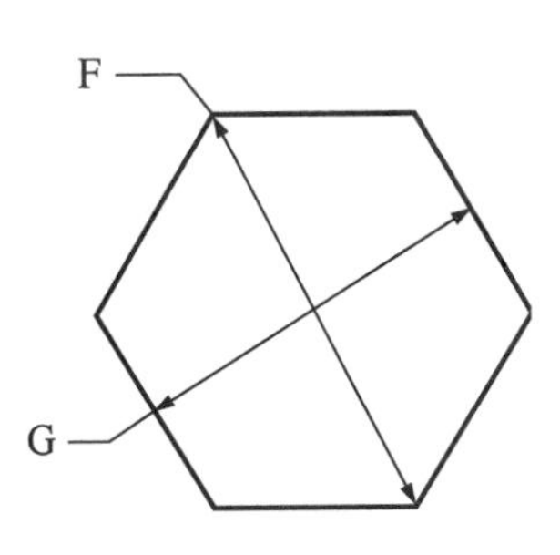

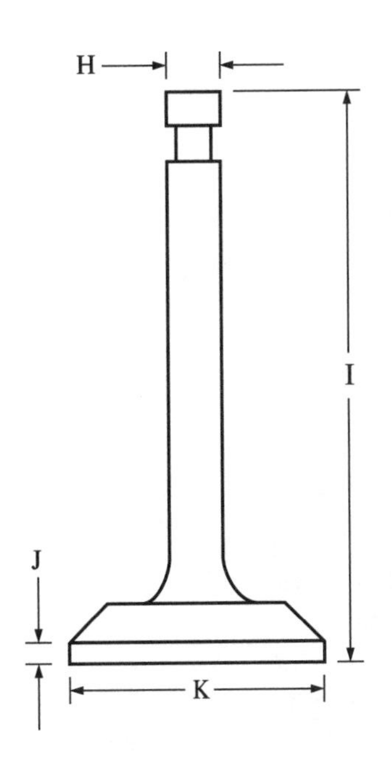

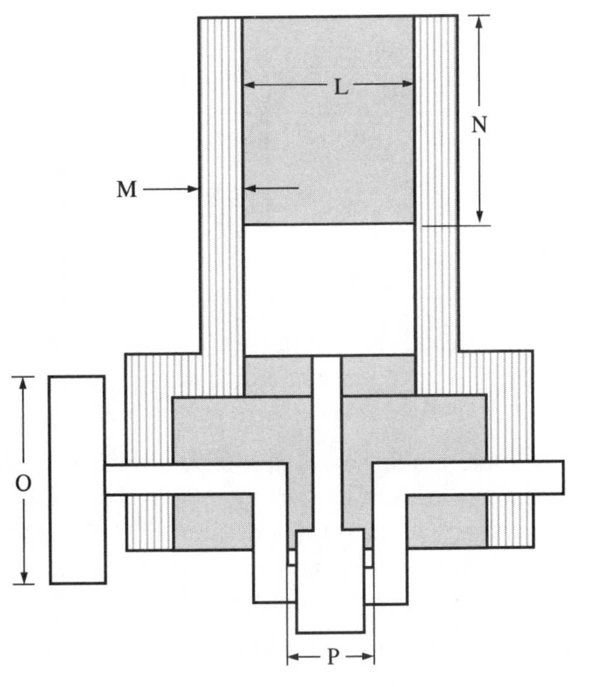

A. Diagonal = ____________________

B. Height = ____________________

C. Width = ____________________

D. Circle diameter = ____________________

E. Circle radius = ____________________

F. Bolt head point-to-point = ____________________

G. Across the flats of bolt head = ____________________

H. Valve stem diameter = ____________________

I. Valve stem length = ____________________

J. Valve margin = ____________________

K. Valve head size = ____________________

L. Cylinder bore = ____________________

M. Wall thickness = ____________________

N. Piston stroke = ____________________

O. Flywheel diameter = ____________________

P. Connecting rod journal width = ____________________

Q. Bolt length = ____________________

R. Size = ____________________

S. Thread length = ____________________

Completed ☐

It is quite common for the small engine technician to convert fractions to decimals or decimals to fractions. Dimensions smaller than 1/64 of an inch should be shown in decimal form. A conversion chart is a convenient way to change from fractions to decimals and from decimals to fractions.

3. Turn to page 475 in your textbook and refer to the Decimal Equivalent Chart to complete the following table.

Fraction	Decimals
1/4	
	.625
3/16	
	.25
7/32	

Completed ❑

4. Turn to page 474 in your textbook and refer to the Millimeter Conversion Chart to complete the following table.

mm	Inches
	.0197
10	
	1.0039
	1.4173
20	

Completed ❑

5. Unlock the thumb screw of a telescoping gauge and depress the spindle part way and lock it in that location. Use an outside micrometer and measure the distance from the spindle face to the anvil face. What does it measure? _____ Completed ❑

6. Use a micrometer to measure the thickness of a feeler gauge blade. Does your reading correspond to the thickness of the blade? _____ If not, clean the blade and the micrometer measuring surfaces and measure again. Does your reading correspond now? _____ If not, check the calibration of the micrometer (See page 30 of text, Cleaning and Calibrating a Micrometer). Completed ❑

7. Use a metric micrometer and measure the diameter of a bolt shank or another smooth cylindrical object. The reading is _____ mm. Completed ❑

8. Measure the thickness of this page with a micrometer that measures in thousandths of an inch. _____″. Measure page thickness in millimeters. _____ mm Completed ❑

9. Attach the magnetic base of a dial indicator to a surface plate or to another clean, flat metal surface. Place a parallel bar or some other straight metal bar on the surface plate. Adjust the dial indicator so that the spindle touches the top of the metal bar. Slide the metal bar along the plate. Is there any change in the reading showing on the dial face? _____ If so, how much? _____ Completed ❑

10. Pick out a random bolt and measure its diameter and thread pitch with a thread pitch gauge. Diameter _____ Pitch _____ Completed ❑

11. Clamp a .50-13 UNC × 2 hex head bolt in a machinist's vise. Use a torque wrench and a socket to apply 20 ft-lb of torque to the bolt. The equivalent torque in inch pounds would be _____. Completed ❑

Instructor's Initials ____________________

Date ____________________

Cleaning, Inspecting, and Measuring Engine Parts

Name ______________________________

Date ____________________ Score________

Instructor ___________________________

Introduction

After an engine has been disassembled, all parts should be thoroughly cleaned. Cleaning must be done with care to avoid scraping and gouging the parts with the cleaning tools. After cleaning, all parts should be inspected for damage, and critical parts should be measured for wear. The ability to properly measure engine parts is one of the most important skills a small engine technician can master. The technician must be able to use precision measuring instruments to obtain accurate readings. These readings must be compared to information in the engine service manual to determine whether parts are worn beyond acceptable limits.

For more information on cleaning, inspection, and measurement, refer to the **Small Gas Engines** textbook. The **Small Gas Engines—Inspection, Measurement, Cleaning** video, available from Goodheart-Willcox Publisher, also contains helpful information on this topic.

Objective

After successfully completing this job, you will be able to properly clean, inspect, and measure engine parts.

Materials and Equipment

To complete this job, you will need the following materials and equipment:

- Engine disassembled in Job 3 or Job 4
- Parts cleaning tank
- Cleaning brush
- Clean shop rags
- Gasket and carbon removal tool
- Wire brush
- Compressed air
- Electric drill with a rotary brush
- Bench grinder with wire wheels
- Shallow pans
- Small parts containers
- Ring groove cleaning tool
- Flat metal surface
- Combination square
- Thickness gauge
- Outside micrometers
- Small hole gauges
- Telescoping gauges
- Dial or vernier caliper
- Service manual for the particular engine you are servicing

Instructions

In this job, you will clean, inspect, and measure the parts of the engine disassembled in Job 3 or . 4. As you read the job procedures, perform the tasks and answer all questions. As you complete each nu mbered step, place a check mark in the corresponding box. This will help you keep track of your progress. When you finish the job, ask your instructor to inspect your work and initial your completed job sheet.

Before performing this job, review all pertinent safety information in the text and discuss safety procedures with your instructor.

Procedure

Cylinder Block, Cover Service

I—0210

1. Use a stiff brush and solvent to clean heavy deposits from the cylinder block. Completed ❑
2. Inspect the cylinder block for damage and wear. Be sure to check the cylinder bore for scuffing or scoring. Examine all threaded holes for damaged threads. If the valves are located in the block, check the valve seats for erosion, leakage, and tightness. On two-cycle engines, check the ports for damage. Completed ❑
3. Measure cylinder bore wear, **Figure 6-1.** Take measurements in six places.

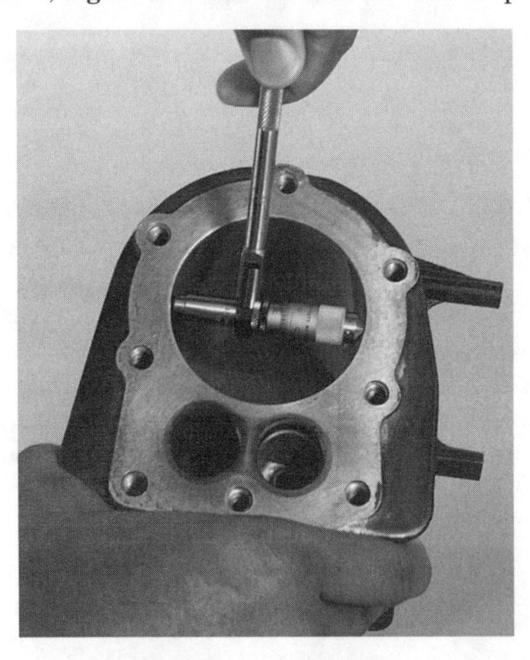

Figure 6-1. *Cylinder diameter can be measured with an inside micrometer equipped with an extension handle. Other measuring tools can be used to check cylinder diameter.*

What tool did you use to take the measurements? ____________________

Cylinder bore diameter (you should have six dimensions): ____________________

____

Manufacturer's specification: ____________________

Is the cylinder worn beyond specifications? ____________________ Completed ❑

Name ______________________________________

4. Carefully remove the crankcase seals. Completed ❑
5. Measure the crankshaft bearing bore.

   What tool did you use to take the measurements? ______________________

   Crankshaft bearing bore diameter:______________________________________

   Manufacturer's specification:____

   Is the bore worn beyond specifications? _____________________________ Completed ❑
6. Measure camshaft bearing bore.

   What tool did you use to take the measurements? ______________________

   Camshaft bearing bore diameter:_______________________________________

   Manufacturer's specification:____

   Is the bore worn beyond specifications? _____________________________ Completed ❑
7. If the valves are located in the cylinder block, measure the valve guide inside diameters.

   What tool did you use to take the measurements? ______________________

   Valve guide diameters:____

   Manufacturer's specification:____

   Are the valve guide inside diameters within specifications? _______________ Completed ❑
8. Remove the remaining gaskets with an abrasive pad and a scraper. Be careful not to gouge the mating surfaces. Completed ❑
9. Hone the cylinder wall to the desired cross-hatch pattern. Completed ❑
10. After honing, clean the cylinder walls with warm, soapy water. Be sure to remove all honing residue. Completed ❑
11. Pour a small amount of clean engine oil on a clean white cloth and wipe off the cylinder walls. Completed ❑
12. Repeat step 11 until there is no residue on the cloth after wiping the cylinder. Completed ❑

Cylinder Head Service

I—1025

13. Clean heavy deposits from the cylinder head using a stiff brush and clean solvent. Use a wire brush mounted in a drill to remove carbon deposits from the underside of the head. Be sure to remove carbon from valve port areas. Completed ❑
14. Inspect the head for cracks and other damage. If the head is from an overhead valve engine, examine the valve seats for erosion, leakage, and tightness. Completed ❑

15. If applicable, measure the inside diameter of each valve guide. See **Figure 6-2.**

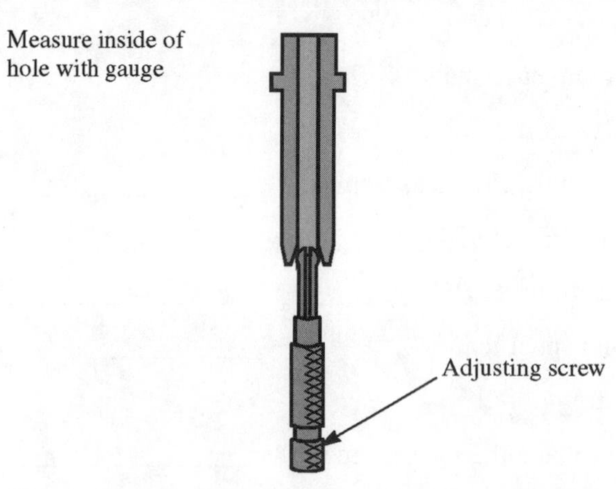

Figure 6-2. *The inside diameter of a valve guide can be measured with a small hole gauge. (Deere & Co.)*

Valve guide diameters:____________________

Manufacturer's specification:____________________

Are the valve guide inside diameters within specifications? __________ Completed ☐

16. Check the flatness of the cylinder head.

What tool did you use to take the measurement? __________

Cylinder head flatness:____________________

Manufacturer's specification:____________________

Is cylinder head flatness within specifications? __________ Completed ☐

Piston, Rod, Crankshaft Service

I—1230

17. Check the piston for signs of physical damage. Pay particular attention to the head, skirts, ring lands, ring grooves, pin boss, and pin hole. Completed ☐

18. Measure the diameter of the piston.

What tool did you use to take the measurement? __________

Piston diameter: ____________________

Manufacturer's specification:____________________

Is the piston diameter within specifications? Completed ☐

Name ______________________________

19. Use a ring expander to remove the piston rings from the piston, **Figure 6-3.** Be careful not to break the rings. Aluminum pistons are easily cut and scored. Completed ❑

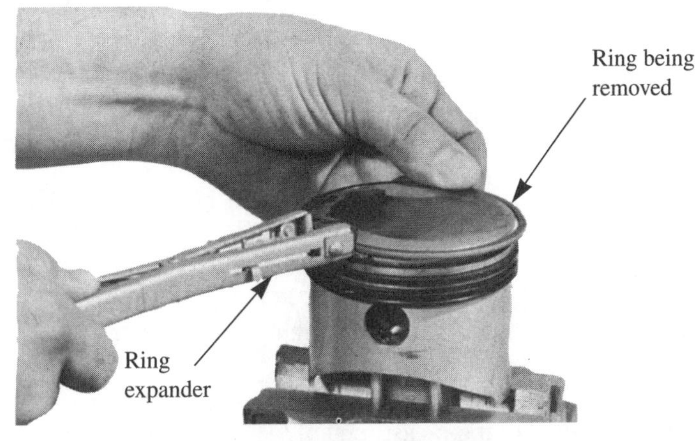

Figure 6-3. *To prevent piston damage, an expander should be used to remove the piston rings. (Tecumseh Products Co.)*

20. Scrape all carbon deposits from the piston head. If the head is flat or slightly domed, carbon can be removed with a carbon scraper or 1 1/4″ wide putty knife. Cleaning contoured piston heads may require the use of a tool with a rounded end, such as a butter knife. Be very careful not to gouge the head, sides, or edges of the piston. Completed ❑

21. Clean the ring grooves with a ring groove cleaning tool or a broken ring from the same groove. Use the correct cleaning tool blade. Never widen or deepen the ring grooves. Completed ❑

22. Measure ring groove side clearance.

    What tool did you use to take the measurements?______________________________

    Side clearance:

    Top groove: ______________________________

    Middle groove: ______________________________

    Bottom groove: ______________________________

    Manufacturer's specifications:

    Top groove: ______________________________

    Middle groove: ______________________________

    Bottom groove: ______________________________

    Are piston ring groove widths within specifications?____________________ Completed ❑

23. Remove the piston pin from the piston and connecting rod assembly. Completed ❑

24. Wash the piston, connecting rod, and piston pin in clean solvent. Completed ❑

25. Examine the connecting rod bearing surfaces for scoring, galling, and discoloration. Completed ❑

26. Measure connecting rod big-end diameter.

    What tool did you use to take the measurement? ____________________

    Connecting rod big-end diameter: ____________________

    Manufacturer's specification: ____________________

    Is the connecting rod big-end diameter within specifications? ____________ Completed ❑

27. Measure connecting rod small-end diameter. ____________________

    What tool did you use to take the measurement? ____________________

    Connecting rod small-end diameter: ____________________

    Manufacturer's specification: ____________________

    Is the connecting rod small-end diameter within specifications? ____________ Completed ❑

28. Measure the piston pin bore.

    What tool did you use to take the measurement? ____________________

    Piston pin bore diameter: ____________________

    Manufacturer's specification: ____________________

    Is the piston pin bore diameter within specifications? ____________ Completed ❑

29. Measure the diameter of the piston pin.

    What tool did you use to take the measurement? ____________________

    Piston pin diameter: ____________________

    Manufacturer's specification: ____________________

    Is the piston pin diameter within specifications? ____________ Completed ❑

30. Inspect the crankshaft for damage. Pay special attention to the snout, the keyway, and the drive end. Examine the bearing surfaces for scoring, galling, and discoloration. Check the crankshaft gear for worn or broken teeth. Completed ❑

31. Measure the diameter of the crankshaft rod journal.

    What tool did you use to take the measurement? ____________________

    Crankshaft rod journal diameter: ____________________

    Manufacturer's specification: ____________________

    Is the crankshaft rod journal diameter within specifications? ____________ Completed ❑

32. Measure the diameter of each crankshaft main bearing journal.

    What tool did you use to take the measurements? ____________________

    Main bearing journal diameters: ____________________

    Manufacturer's specification: ____________________

    Are the main bearing journals within specifications? ____________ Completed ❑

33. Wash the crankshaft in clean solvent and blow it dry with compressed air. Be sure to blow out any oil holes in the crankshaft. Completed ❑

Name ______________________________

Oil Pump Service

I—1720

If the engine has an oil pump, perform steps 34-37.

34. Measure the oil pump rotor-to-body clearance.

    What tool did you use to take the measurement? ____________________

    Rotor-to-body clearance: ____________________

    Manufacturer's specification: ____________________

    Is the rotor-to-body clearance within specifications? ____________________ Completed ☐

35. Measure the diameter of the oil pump shaft.

    What tool did you use to take the measurement? ____________________

    Oil pump shaft diameter: ____________________

    Manufacturer's specification: ____________________

    Is the oil pump shaft diameter within specifications? ____________________ Completed ☐

36. Measure the thickness of the oil pump rotor.

    What tool did you use to take the measurement? ____________________

    Rotor thickness: ____________________

    Manufacturer's specification: ____________________

    Is rotor thickness within specifications? ____________________ Completed ☐

37. Measure clearance between the oil pump cover and the rotor face.

    What tool did you use to take the measurement? ____________________

    Rotor-to-cover clearance: ____________________

    Manufacturer's specification: ____________________

    Is rotor-to-cover clearance within specifications? ____________________ Completed ☐

Valve Train Service

I—1755

38. Visually inspect the valves for damage. Completed ☐

39. Use a wire brush mounted in a bench grinder to clean carbon deposits from the head and neck of each valve. Completed ☐

40. Measure the diameters of the valve stems, **Figure 6-4.**

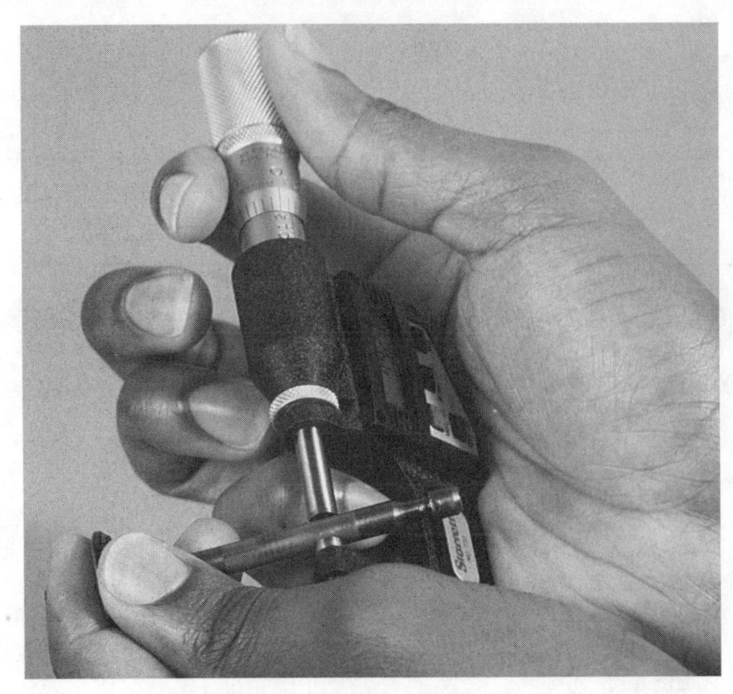

Figure 6-4. *An outside micrometer is used to measure valve stem diameter.*

Valve stem diameters: ____________________

Manufacturer's specification: ____________________

Are the valve stem diameters within specification? ____________________ Completed ❑

41. Measure the valve spring lengths and check the springs for straightness. ______

What tool did you use to take the measurements? ____________________

Valve spring lengths: ____________________

Manufacturer's specification: ____________________

Are the valve spring lengths within specifications? ____________________

Are the valve springs straight? ____________________ Completed ❑

42. Inspect the retainers and keepers for wear. Completed ❑

43. Examine the camshaft for damage and wear. Pay special attention to the shaft ends. Examine the bearing surfaces for scoring, galling, and discoloration. Check the camshaft gear for worn or broken teeth. Completed ❑

44. Measure the cam journal diameters.

What tool did you use to take the measurements? ____________________

Cam journal diameters: ____________________

Manufacturer's specification: ____________________

Are the cam journals within specifications? ____________________ Completed ❑

Name ______________________________

45. Measure the cam lobes.

    What tool did you use to take the measurements? ____________________

    Cam lobe dimensions: ______________________________

    Manufacturer's specification:______________________________

    Are the lobes within specifications? ____________________ Completed ☐

46. Inspect the tappets for wear. Completed ☐

47. If you are working with an overhead valve engine, check the straightness of the pushrods. Completed ☐

48. Inspect the rocker arms for damage. Completed ☐

49. Order all new parts needed to reassemble the engine. All worn or damaged parts must be serviced or replaced. Completed ☐

Instructor's Initials____________________

Date ____________________

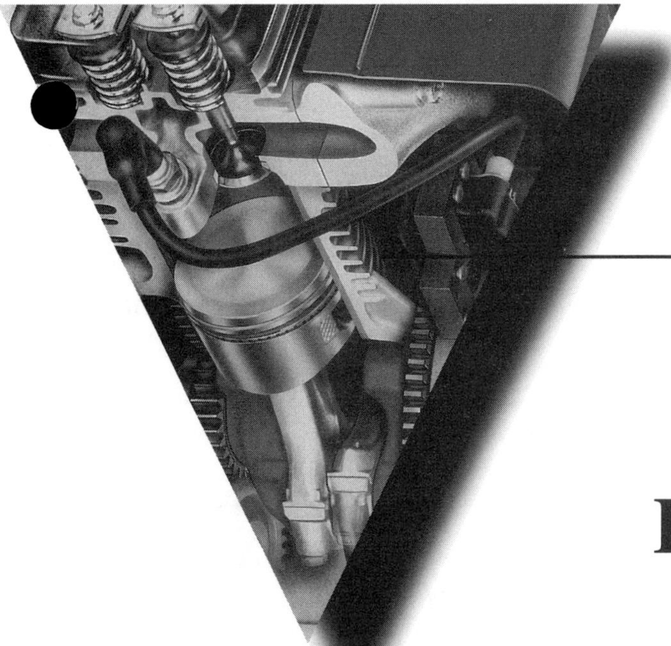

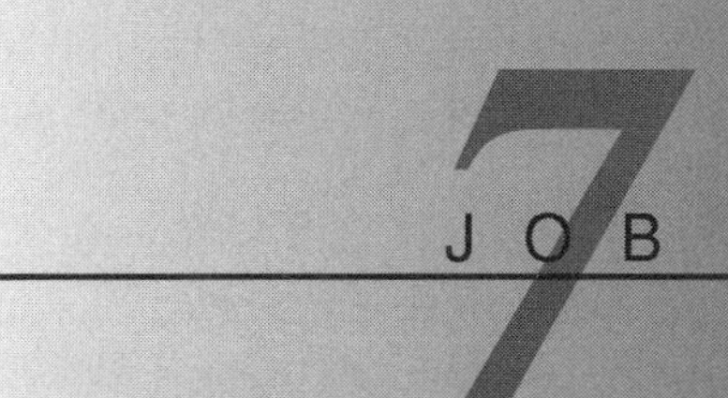

Four-Cycle Engine Reassembly

Name ______________________________

Date ____________________ Score________

Instructor ___________________________

Introduction

After inspecting engine parts and replacing or repairing damaged components, the engine can be reassembled. The reassembly process must be accomplished very carefully if the engine is to operate correctly.

Objective

After successfully completing this job, you will be able to properly assemble a four-cycle engine.

Materials and Equipment

To complete this job, you will need the following materials and equipment:

- Appropriate engine service manual
- New crankcase seals and sealer
- Wood blocks
- Seal drivers
- Retaining ring pliers
- Torque wrench
- Socket set
- Combination, box, and open-end wrenches
- Screwdrivers
- Thickness gauges
- Valve stem grinder
- Vee blocks
- Valve spring compressor
- Valve stem seals
- Rebuild gasket kit
- Machinist's vise with soft jaw covers
- New piston rings (if needed)
- Ring expander
- Hammer
- Pliers
- Heavy grease
- Gasket adhesive
- New head bolt washers and seals (if needed)
- Valve stem caps (for OHV engines)
- Strap wrench or flywheel tool
- New flywheel key
- Fuel line
- New fuel filter
- New air filter cartridge
- Brass air gap gauge
- New muffler gasket
- Correct motor oil
- Fire extinguisher
- Fuel

Instructions

In this job, you will reassemble the engine disassembled in Job 3, Four-Cycle Engine Disassembly. Before beginning this job, review the chapters in the **Small Gas Engines** textbook that provide information about the various engine parts you are about to assemble. Refer to the engine service manual for detailed information about the engine you are assembling. The **Small Gas Engines—Reassembly** video will also be helpful.

As you complete each numbered step, place a check mark in the corresponding box. This will help you keep track of your progress. When you finish the job, ask your instructor to inspect your work and initial your completed job sheet.

Before performing this job, review all pertinent safety information in the text and discuss safety procedures with your instructor.

Procedures

R—0140

Crankshaft Seals and Oil Pump Installation

1. Install the new crankshaft seals in the crankcase. Make sure the seals are the right size. For metal body seals, coat the outside with a sealer. Place the crankcase on wood blocks so damage does not occur while driving in the new seals. Select a seal driver that is slightly smaller than the outside diameter of the seal. Drive the seal in until it seats squarely but lightly. See **Figure 7-1.** Rubber seals do not need a sealer. Instead, coat the seals with oil.

Completed ❑

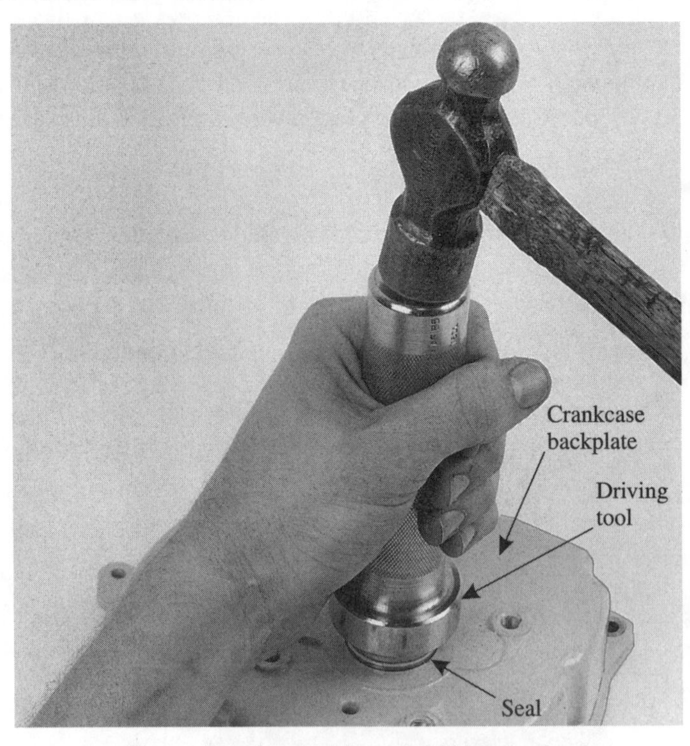

Figure 7-1. *A seal driver should be used when installing new seals. (Deere & Co.)*

2. Install the governor flyweight assembly. Flyweights should fly out freely when spun by hand. Oil the flyweight assembly. Completed ❑

3. If the engine has an oil pump, lubricate the pump parts and put them into place. A snap ring may secure the shaft. Be sure the ring snaps into the groove on the shaft. Completed ❑

Name ____________________________________

4. Fit a new gasket onto the pump cover and bolt the cover into place. Tighten the bolts or screws to the recommended torque. Completed ❑
5. If there is an oil pressure relief valve, lubricate it, install it, and tighten the cover nut. Completed ❑

Crankshaft and Piston Installation

R—0800

6. Coat all machined crankshaft and crankcase surfaces with heavy motor oil. Completed ❑
7. Being careful not to damage the new seal, place the crankshaft into the main bore of the crankcase. Completed ❑
8. Assemble the piston onto the connecting rod. Look for alignment marks on the piston dome and the connecting rod. They must match in direction. Completed ❑
9. Clamp the rod lightly in a vise that has soft jaw covers. Install one snap ring in the piston pin hole. Completed ❑
10. Oil the pin and press it through the piston and the small end of the connecting rod. Completed ❑
11. Install the second snap ring, making sure both snap rings are locked in their grooves. Completed ❑
12. Install the piston rings. Read the instructions that come with the new rings. Rings must be oriented correctly in their grooves. Identify the top of each ring. Use a ring expander tool to expand the rings just enough to fit over the piston. Piston rings are brittle and will break if expanded excessively. Install the oil ring first in the lowest groove. Install the compression rings in the upper grooves. Completed ❑
13. Apply oil liberally to the piston rings and the piston. Completed ❑
14. Space the ring gaps about 120° to one another. Completed ❑
15. Install the piston and rod in the cylinder block. Use a ring compressor to squeeze the rings into the grooves. This will allow the piston to slide into the cylinder. Place the tool around the piston and rings and tighten the tool. Completed ❑
16. Insert the rod through the cylinder until the compressor seats on the cylinder block. Make sure the piston and rod are facing the correct direction. Use a hammer handle to press the piston into the cylinder while guiding the rod so it seats squarely on the crankshaft journal. See **Figure 7-2.** Completed ❑

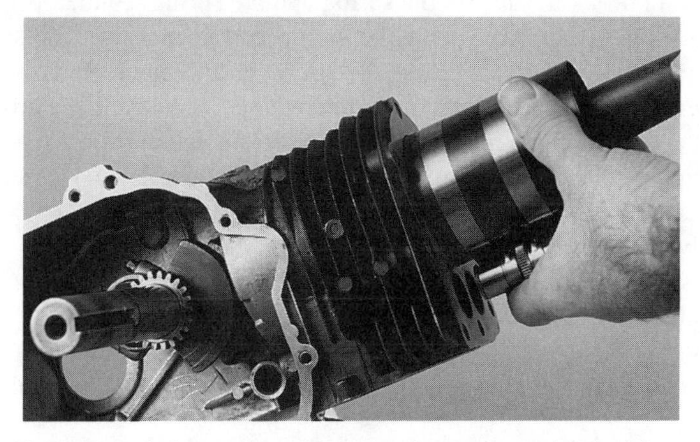

Figure 7-2. *A ring compressor is used to squeeze the rings into the grooves, allowing the piston to be pushed into the cylinder.*

17. Oil the rod cap and place it and the oil slinger over the journal. Be sure the alignment mark on the cap is aligned with the mark on the rod. Install the two rod cap bolts finger tight. Then, torque the bolts to specifications. Completed ❑

18. With pliers, bend the locking tabs against the bolt heads to prevent them from loosening. Completed ❑

Camshaft and Valve Lifter Installation

R—1236

19. Apply a heavy grease to the valve lifters and install them in the proper lifter bores in the block. The grease will keep the lifters in place during camshaft installation. Completed ❑

20. Coat the camshaft and cam lobes with grease. Turn the crankshaft so the timing mark on the timing gear faces the camshaft bore. Install the camshaft in the camshaft bore so that the camshaft gear timing mark aligns with the crankshaft timing mark. Completed ❑

21. Place a new crankcase gasket over the crankcase dowel pins. If there are no dowels, put a thin coating of adhesive on the gasket to hold it in place until the cover has been installed. Completed ❑

22. Carefully guide the seals over the crankshaft while lowering the crankcase cover onto the gasket. Torque the cover bolts to specifications in a crisscross pattern. Completed ❑

Completed ❑

Valve Installation

R—0430

23. Install the valves.

For valve-in-block engines:

A. Insert the valves in the valve guides. Be sure to place the exhaust and intake valves in their correct locations. They must not be reversed during installation. Completed ❑

B. Turn the crankshaft until the valve tappet is all the way up and the other tappet is all the way down. Completed ❑

C. Use a thickness gage to check the clearance between the closed valve and the tappet (valve clearance). If the clearance is too small, the valve stem must be ground until the clearance is correct. Do not grind too much. A thousandth or two at a time is enough. Use vee blocks and a grinder. Completed ❑

D. Place the valve springs and the retainers over the valve stems. Check to see if the springs are interchangeable. Sometimes the exhaust spring is longer than the intake spring and must be installed accordingly. Refer to the service manual. Completed ❑

E. Use a spring compressor to squeeze the spring and the spring retainer, **Figure 7-3.** Slide the valve upward and place the spring and keeper over the stem. Unscrew the compressor tool to release the spring and retainer. Remove the tool. Make sure the small end of the hole in the retainer is locked in the groove of the valve stem. Repeat this procedure on the second valve. Completed ❑

F. Install the breather cover. Make sure the oil drain holes face down. Use a new gasket and install screws. Completed ❑

For overhead-valve engines:

A. Oil the valve stems and place them into the valve guides. Completed ❑

B. Install new valve stem seals over the stems and onto the head. Completed ❑

C. Place the valve spring and retainer over the valve stem. Use a C-clamp spring compressor to squeeze the spring coils together. Hold the tool squarely in place. Completed ❑

Name ____

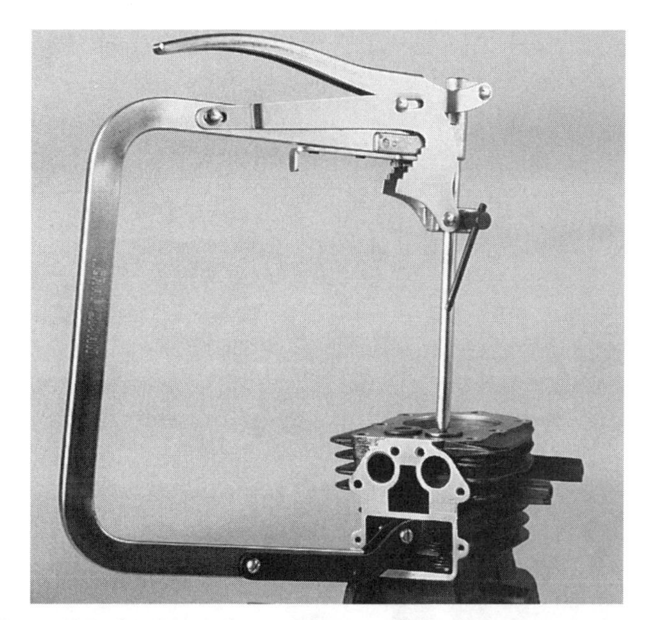

Figure 7-3. *A valve spring compressor is used to squeeze the valve spring and retainer, allowing installation of the keepers.*

D. Place one keeper in the recess of the retainer and the valve stem groove. Place the second keeper in place, holding it with your finger while releasing the spring compressor. Be sure both keepers are locked into the groove around the valve stem. Completed ❑

E. Repeat this procedure on the second valve. Completed ❑

Cylinder Head Installation

R—1700

24. Install the cylinder head and related components.

For a valve-in-block engine:

A. Place a new cylinder head gasket on the block. Make sure that all the holes are aligned properly. Do not use sealer on the head or the gasket. Completed ❑

B. Set the head on the gasket. Completed ❑

C. Lubricate the cylinder head bolts and start them in their proper holes. Some bolts may be longer than others and must be installed in specific locations. Completed ❑

D. Use a torque wrench to tighten all the head bolts in a crisscross pattern. Refer to the service manual for amount of torque and exact sequence of tightening. Completed ❑

For an overhead valve engine:

A. Install a new cylinder head gasket on the block. Make sure that all the holes are aligned properly. Do not use sealer on the head or gasket. Completed ❑

B. Carefully set the head on the block. Be careful not to damage the gasket. Completed ❑

C. Lubricate the cylinder head bolts. Insert the bolts and start them in their proper holes. Some head bolts may have special metal washers with rubber seals on them. If so, use new washers and seals to prevent oil from seeping down around the bolt threads. Completed ❑

D. Install the push rods. Check to see if one of the pushrods has holes at both ends. If so, it must be placed in the correct lifter to carry oil up to the rocker arms. Check the service manual for detailed instructions. Completed ❑

E. Place the stem caps over the valve stems and install the rocker arms onto the rocker arm studs. Make sure the pushrods are seated in the rocker arms. Lubricate all these parts liberally with motor oil. Completed ❑

F. Turn the crankshaft so that the cam lobe is at the lowest position. Adjust rocker arm-to-valve clearance by turning the adjusting nut on the rocker arm stud. At the same time, place the correct thickness gauge leaf between the valve stem cap and the rocker arm. Turn the nut until a slight drag is felt, **Figure 7-4.** Tighten the lock screw with an Allen wrench. Recheck clearance. Repeat this procedure for the second valve.

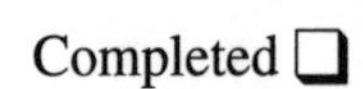

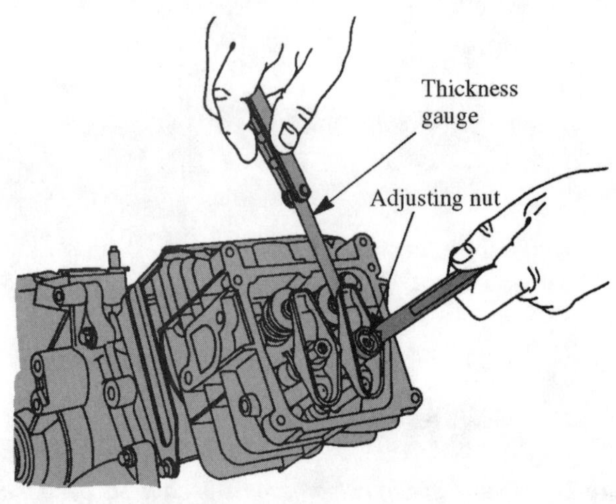

Figure 7-4. *Rocker arm-to-valve clearance is adjusted by turning the adjuster nut until a slight drag is felt on the thickness gauge. (Briggs & Stratton Corp.)*

G. Place a new valve cover gasket on the head and set the cover in place. Install the bolts and torque them to specifications. Overtightening these bolts can warp the cover and cause oil leakage. Completed ❑

R—1945

External Parts Installation

25. Install the ignition components.

On an older engine:

A. Install the points and the condenser. See the **Small Gas Engines** textbook for details. If the coil is mounted outside the flywheel, the air gap must be adjusted during installation. Completed ❑

B. Adjust the breaker point gap. Turn the crankshaft clockwise until the piston is at the proper position in the cylinder on the compression stroke (both valves closed). See **Small Gas Engines**, Chapter 14, *Ignition System Service,* for information on adjusting piston height and adjusting breaker points. Completed ❑

C. Install the breaker point cover. Completed ❑

On a newer engine:

A. Install the solid-state ignition module with the screws provided. Completed ❑

B. Check the air gap for correct spacing. Loosen the screws and adjust with an air gap gauge as needed. Torque screws. Completed ❑

C. Connect the ignition switch wire. Completed ❑

26. Install the flywheel on the crankshaft. Make sure the key is seated properly in its keyway and keyslot. Completed ❑

27. Place the washer on the crankshaft and install the nut or clutch. Use a strap wrench to keep the flywheel from rotating while you torque the nut or clutch. If a clutch is used to secure the flywheel, a special spanner tool and a torque wrench must be used to tighten it. Otherwise, a torque wrench and standard socket can be used to tighten the nut. Completed ❑

Name ______________________________________

28. Install the flywheel screen. Align the holes and install all screws. Completed ❑
29. Install the governor arm onto its shaft. Completed ❑
30. Assemble all governor linkage rods and springs according to your disassembly diagram. Be sure they are all in their correct holes. You may have to install choke and governor linkages before bolting the carburetor to the engine. Completed ❑
31. Install the carburetor. Place the two bolts through the carburetor flange with the gasket in place. Start the bolts by hand and then tighten them with a wrench. Completed ❑
32. Install the fuel line. Move all linkages to make sure they operate freely. Completed ❑
33. Move the throttle to the full-throttle position. Loosen the lock nut on the governor lever and turn the shaft fully clockwise. Tighten the lock nut. See the **Small Gas Engines** textbook for more information on engine governor adjustments. Completed ❑
34. Install the breather tube and breather cover onto the carburetor fitting. If the carburetor is not installed on the fuel tank, install a new fuel line and a new inline fuel filter. Completed ❑
35. Install the air filter case on the carburetor. Insert a new filter cartridge and install the cover. Completed ❑
36. Install the muffler with a new heat-resistant gasket. The shiny side of the gasket should be placed toward the engine. Install the bolts and torque them to proper specifications. Completed ❑
37. Bend any locking tabs to keep the bolts from loosening. Completed ❑
38. Install all shrouds around the cylinder. Completed ❑
39. Bolt on the flywheel shroud. Completed ❑
40. Install any remaining parts, such as pulleys or gears. Completed ❑

Preparing to Start the Engine

R—2340

Before performing the following steps, the engine should be securely fastened to a bench mount or installed on the implement it was removed from. If a bench mount is used, an approved exhaust ventilation system should be connected. If the engine is on an implement, it should be started outdoors or connected to the exhaust ventilation system.

---

41. Install the spark plug and torque it to specifications. Attach the high-tension lead. Completed ❑
42. Make sure the oil drain plug has been replaced and tightened. Fill the crankcase with the recommended viscosity and quantity of motor oil. Close the oil filler plug or install the dip stick and cap. Inspect for any oil leaks. Completed ❑
43. Add a quantity of fuel to the fuel tank. Examine the fuel lines and tank for fuel leaks. Completed ❑

Safe practice dictates that a charged fire extinguisher be located near the engine on initial start-up.

---

44. Unless the carburetor has been preset at the factory, it will need to be adjusted for starting, high speed, and idle operation. The idle speed screw will also need to be adjusted for proper RPM. Refer to the service manual for initial carburetor needle setting and further adjustment procedures. Let the engine warm up before making final adjustments. Completed ❑

45. Break-in the engine as instructed by the manufacturer. Typical break-in recommendations include:
    - Operate the engine at a fast idle until it is warm.
    - Avoid prolonged high-RPM operation.
    - Do not let the engine overheat.
    - Watch for oil leaks.
    - Check the oil level often until rings seat properly. Completed ❑

Instructor's Initials ______________________

Date ______________________

Two-Cycle Engine Reassembly

Name ______________________________

Date ____________________ Score_________

Instructor ____________________________

Introduction

After inspecting engine parts and replacing or repairing damaged components, the engine can be reassembled. The reassembly process must be accomplished very carefully if the engine is to operate correctly.

Objective

After successfully completing this job, you will be able to properly assemble a two-cycle engine.

Materials and Equipment

To complete this job, you will need the following materials and equipment:

- Appropriate engine service manual
- Crankshaft bore seals and sealer
- Seal drivers
- New piston rings
- Ring expander
- Motor oil
- Retaining ring pliers
- New connecting rod bearings
- Torque wrench
- Socket set
- Screwdrivers
- Pliers
- Combination, box, and open-end wrenches
- New gasket kit
- Gasket sealer
- Thickness gauges
- Machinist's vise with soft jaw covers
- Strap wrench or flywheel tool
- New flywheel key
- Fuel line
- New fuel filter
- New air filter cartridge
- New muffler gasket
- New reed valve (if needed)
- New reed valve O-ring seal or gasket
- Grease
- Brass air gap gauge
- Fire extinguisher
- Proper oil/fuel mixture.

Instructions

In this job, the engine disassembled in Job 4 will be reassembled. Before beginning this job, review the chapters in the **Small Gas Engines** textbook that provide information about the various engine parts you are about to assemble. Refer to the engine service manual for detailed information about the engine you are assembling. The **Small Gas Engines—Reassembly** video will also be helpful.

As you complete each numbered step, place a check mark in the corresponding box. This will help you keep track of your progress. When you finish the job, ask your instructor to inspect your work and initial your completed job sheet.

Before performing this job, review all pertinent safety information in the text and discuss safety procedures with your instructor.

Procedures

R—0800

Crankshaft and Piston Installation

1. Install new crankshaft bore seals in the crankcase and the crankcase cover. Completed ❑
2. Assemble the piston assembly. Check for alignment marks on the piston dome and the connecting rod. These marks must match in direction. Completed ❑
3. Install new piston rings on the piston. Follow the instructions that come with the new rings. Rings must be oriented correctly in their grooves. Use a ring expander to expand rings just enough to fit over the piston. Completed ❑
4. Install new bearings on the crankpin of the crankshaft. Completed ❑
5. Insert piston and rod into crankcase. Completed ❑
6. With the crankpin positioned at the top dead center position, insert the crankshaft into the crankcase while carefully sliding the big end of the connecting rod over the crank arm and onto the crankpin. See **Figure 8-1.** Completed ❑

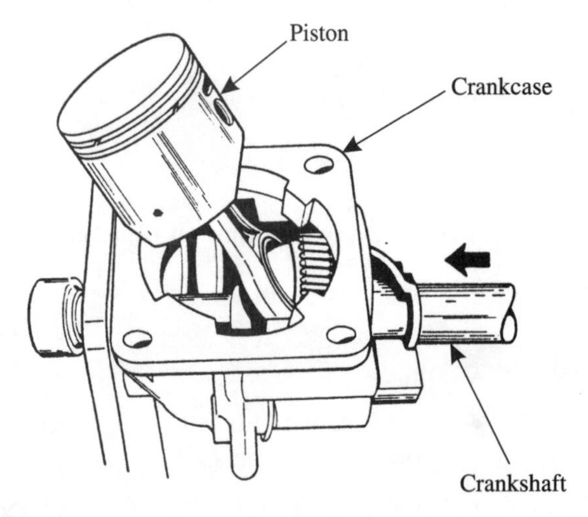

Figure 8-1. *Insert the crankshaft into the crankcase while carefully sliding the big end of the connecting rod onto the crankpin. (Tecumseh Products Co.)*

7. If recommended, apply sealer to the mating surface of the crankcase cover. Completed ❑
8. Install the crankcase cover on the crankcase and tighten all fasteners to the recommended torque. Completed ❑

Name ____

Cylinder Installation

9. Apply recommended sealer to the crankcase-to-cylinder mating surface. The sealer must completely surround bolt holes. Completed ❑

10. Position the cylinder correctly and slowly push it onto the piston. See **Figure 8-2.** Compress the piston rings by hand as you install the cylinder. Completed ❑

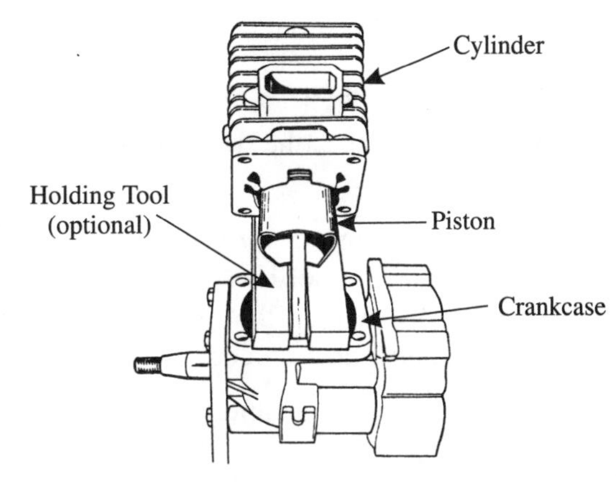

Figure 8-2. *Make sure the cylinder is in the correct position before pushing it onto the piston. Do not rotate the cylinder during installation. (Tecumseh Products Co.)*

11. Torque all cylinder fasteners to specifications. Completed ❑

External Part Installation

R—1945

12. Install the muffler. Use a new heat-resistant gasket. The shiny side of the gasket should face the engine. Install all fasteners and torque them to specifications. Completed ❑

13. Bend any locking tabs to keep the muffler fasteners from loosening. Completed ❑

14. Install the muffler heat shield. Completed ❑

15. Install a new reed valve. Place a new O-ring seal around the valve and coat the seal with grease. Press the valve into the recess on the side of the crankcase. Completed ❑

16. Install the blower housing base. Torque all base fasteners to specifications. Completed ❑

17. If removed, reinstall the governor air vane assembly in the blower housing base. Completed ❑

18. Assemble all governor linkage rods and springs according to your disassembly diagram. Be sure they are in their correct holes. Completed ❑

19. Reinstall the carburetor and spacer. Use a new gasket and torque the carburetor gaskets to specifications. Completed ❑

20. Install the flywheel onto the crankshaft. Be sure to use a new flywheel key. Completed ❑

21. Hold the flywheel with a strap wrench and torque the flywheel nut to specifications. Completed ❑

22. Reinstall the ignition module and adjust the air gap between the module and the flywheel. Completed ❑

23. Install the flywheel shroud, the screen shield, and the recoil starter. Completed ❑

24. Install the fuel tank and connect the fuel line between the tank and the carburetor. Completed ❑

Preparing to Start the Engine

R—2340

Before performing the following steps, the engine should be securely fastened to a bench mount or installed on the implement it came from. If a bench mount is used, an approved exhaust ventilation system should be connected. If the engine is on an implement, it should be started outdoors or connected to the exhaust ventilation system.

---

25. Install the spark plug and torque it to specifications. Completed ❑
26. Attach the high tension lead to the spark plug. Completed ❑
27. Fill the fuel tank with a fuel/oil mixture. Check the fuel lines and the tank for leaks. Completed ❑
28. Unless the carburetor has been preset at the factory, it must be adjusted for starting, high-speed operation, and idle operation. The idle speed screw must also be adjusted to obtain the proper RPM. Refer to the service manual for initial carburetor needle setting and further adjustment procedures. Completed ❑
29. Start the engine and allow it to warm up before making final adjustments. Completed ❑
30. Break-in the engine as recommended by the manufacturer. Typical break-in instructions include:
    - Operate the engine at a fast idle until it is warm.
    - Avoid prolonged high-RPM operation.
    - Do not let the engine overheat. Completed ❑

Instructor's Initials ______________________

Date ______________________

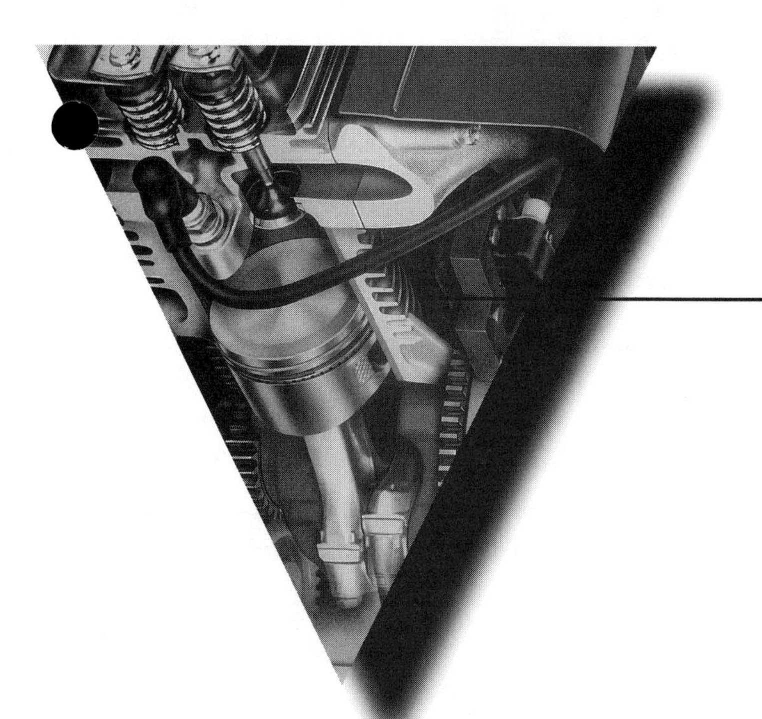

General Engine Troubleshooting

Name ______________________________

Date ____________________ Score_________

Instructor ____________________________

Introduction

Millions of small engines are used in hundreds of applications by homeowners, industries, and construction companies. Most small gas engines get minimal attention. Many times, an engine is used until it finally shows obvious signs of trouble or stops running altogether. Most people are not equipped to diagnose and correct small engine problems. Instead, they take the implement to a technician for this service. The following job will introduce procedures for identifying many common engine problems and how to correct them.

A primary rule for troubleshooting is to start with the simplest and most logical causes. Do not begin disassembling parts of the engine until you have isolated the problem. Do a complete examination. It is quite possible that the engine has more than one problem.

Objective

After successfully completing this job, you will be able to isolate, analyze, and diagnose engine problems.

Materials and Equipment

To complete this job, you will need the following materials and equipment:

- Engine that has been in service and preferably indicates some sort of problems(s)
- Troubleshooting chart in text or service manual
- Ratchet wrench
- Spark plug socket
- Torque wrench
- Compression tester
- Spark tester

Instructions

This job is best accomplished with an engine that has been used for a long period of time and may have problems. The engine may only need general service. However, an engine that has real problems will give the best experience.

Before starting this job, review Chapter 12, Preventive Maintenance and Troubleshooting, in your **Small Gas Engines** textbook. The **Small Gas Engines—Troubleshooting & Tune-Up** video, available from Goodheart-Willcox Publisher, will also be helpful.

As you read the job procedures, perform the tasks and answer all questions. As you complete each numbered step, place a check mark in the corresponding box. This will help you keep track of your progress. When you finish the job, ask your instructor to inspect your work and initial your completed job sheet.

Before performing this job, review all pertinent safety information in the text and discuss safety procedures with your instructor.

Procedure

T—0215

Troubleshooting

1. Before attempting to start the engine, check for obvious problems, such as a locked-up or seized engine, fluid leaks, etc. Look for fuel leaks around the carburetor, fuel lines, and connections. Check for wetness under the fuel bowl. Deteriorated seals, gaskets, and hoses, as well as a high float level, can cause fuel leakage and rich running.

   List any problems found. ______________________________

   ______________________________ Completed ❑

2. Correct the problems found in step 1. Completed ❑

3. If the engine is operable, start it and check operation. Completed ❑

T—0545

Exhaust Smoke

4. If the engine runs roughly and produces a black exhaust smoke, the carburetor may be set too rich, the choke may be in a partially closed position, or the air filter may be clogged with dirt. Observe the exhaust and answer the following questions.

   A. What color is the exhaust? ______________________________

   B. What does the color suggest about the engine? ______________________________ Completed ❑

T—0610

Abnormal Noises

5. As the engine is running, listen for unusual noises, such as rod knock (wear between rod bore and crank journal), piston slap (excessive piston to cylinder clearance), piston pin knock (excessive clearance between piston pin, connecting rod, and piston boss), or valve clatter (excessive clearance between valve stem and rocker arm). List any unusual noises heard. ______________________________

   ______________________________ Completed ❑

Name ______________________________________

Operating Requirements

T—0305

6. If the engine will not start, perform the following tests.
   A. **Check for proper compression.** There should be 30-35 psi pressure on the compression stroke for starting. A quick way to check compression is to crank the engine. If the compression is low, the crankshaft will spin easily with little resistance. A compression tester can also be used. Remove the spark plug, insert the compression tester stem into the spark plug hole, and crank the engine. The needle on the dial face will give an accurate compression reading. Completed ❑
   B. **Check ignition system operation.** Remove the spark plug and install a spark tester or ground the spark plug on the engine. Crank the engine and look for a hot spark across the spark plug electrode gap. The spark should be bright blue. If there is no spark, check the engine shut-off wire and other ignition system elements. Check the coil, ground, or stop wires for shorts. Completed ❑
   C. **Check for fuel.** If the ignition system seems to be operating properly but the engine will not start, remove the spark plug and squirt some fuel into the cylinder. Replace the spark plug and try starting the engine. If it starts, then stops, the problem is fuel supply. Check the fuel tank and finger strainer inside the tank, if there is one. Check the fuel valve. Check the condition of the in-line fuel strainer, fuel lines and connections. Look for water in the fuel system. A wet spark plug indicates flooding from a closed choke, high float level clogged air filter, or other carburetion problem. If the plug is dry, fuel may not be entering the combustion chamber. Completed ❑
   D. **Check the lubrication system.** If lubrication level is inadequate, scoring of internal parts will occur and the engine will seize. Make sure the correct amount of recommended oil is used. Look at the color and condition of the oil. Extremely dark oil indicates oil has not been changed at recommended intervals. If engine has an oil filter, check it for excessive contamination. Completed ❑
   E. **Check for cooling system problems.** Lubricating oil is a part of the cooling system. If oil is not the problem, check the cooling fins and shrouds around the cylinder. If they are filled with dirt and debris, the engine will run hot, causing damage to internal parts. If the engine is water cooled, check the radiator, thermostat, water pump, hoses, and connections. Completed ❑
7. List any problems found. ______________________________________

   ____

   ______________________________________ Completed ❑

Refer to the Engine Troubleshooting Chart on page 211 of your **Small Gas Engines** textbook for further information.

Instructor's Initials ____________________

Date ____________________

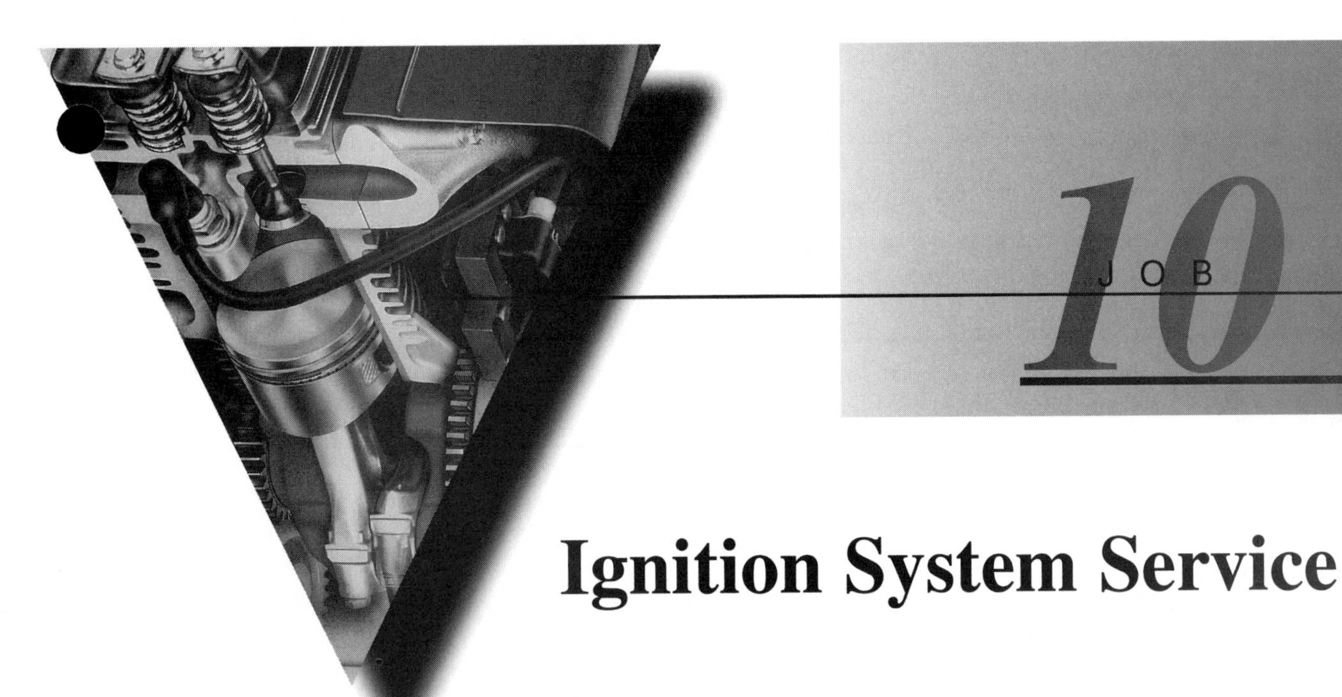

Ignition System Service

Name ________________________________

Date ____________________ Score________

Instructor ____________________________

Introduction

The small engine ignition system requires periodic service. Ignition system service involves testing all the ignition system components and replacing worn or defective parts. In some cases, parts can be cleaned and adjusted.

Objective

After successfully completing this job, you will be able to properly service the ignition system found on a typical small gas engine.

Materials and Equipment

To complete this job, you will need the following materials and equipment:

- Engine
- Ohmmeter
- Ignition tester
- Spark tester
- Flywheel puller
- 9/16" socket
- 6" screwdriver
- Pliers
- Combination, box, and open-end wrenches
- Thickness gauge
- Breaker points
- Condenser
- Coil
- Spark plug
- Solid state pulse transformer
- Solid state ignition module
- Solid state conversion module

Instructions

Before starting this job, refer to Chapters 9 and 14, *Ignition Systems* and *Ignition System Service*, in the **Small Gas Engines** textbook. The **Small Gas Engines—Troubleshooting & Tune-up** video, available from Goodheart-Willcox Publisher, will also be helpful. As you complete each numbered step, place a check mark in the corresponding box. This will help you keep track of your progress. When you finish the job, ask your instructor to inspect your work and initial your completed job sheet.

Before performing this job, review all pertinent safety information in the text and discuss safety procedures with your instructor.

Procedure

Ignition System Service

T—0820

1. Remove the spark plug wire from the plug. Completed ❑
2. Install a spark tester on the plug wire and clip the tester onto the engine. Completed ❑
3. Pull the starter cord while watching the spark produced at the tip of the tester. If there is no spark or a weak spark, the ignition system is faulty. If there is a strong blue spark, the ignition system is working correctly. Remember, however, that this test does not verify the operation of the spark plug. Describe the results of the spark test. ______________________________

   ______________________________ Completed ❑
4. Use a spark plug socket and a ratchet to remove the plug from the engine. Completed ❑
5. Examine the spark plug. Make sure it is the correct plug for the engine. A hot plug has a relatively long insulator and will run hotter than a cold plug. A plug that is too cold will foul with carbon. A plug that is too hot can develop burned electrodes. Does the spark plug show signs of engine problems? ______________ If so, what problems are indicated? ______________

   ______________________________ Completed ❑
6. Clean and gap the electrodes, if necessary. See **Figure 10-1.** Completed ❑

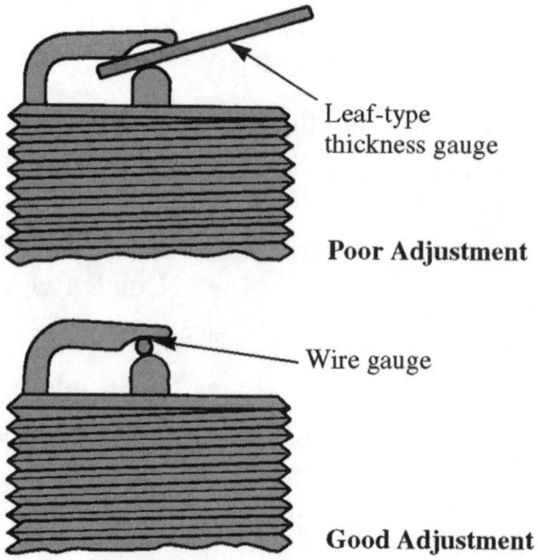

Leaf-type thickness gauge

Poor Adjustment

Wire gauge

Good Adjustment

Figure 10-1. *A wire-type feeler gauge should be used when gapping used spark plugs. A leaf-type gauge may not give an accurate measurement if the plug's electrodes are not flat and parallel.*

Name ______________________________________

7. Replace the spark plug. Torque it to 13-15 lb-ft. Install the spark plug wire on the plug. Completed ❑
8. Remove the flywheel. Completed ❑
9. Examine the key for indications of shearing or distortion. Completed ❑
10. Test the flywheel magnets. Place a 9/16" socket on one of the magnets and tip flywheel. The magnet should hold the socket in place. Perform this test on the other flywheel magnet. If either flywheel magnet is weak, the flywheel must be replaced. Completed ❑

Breaker Points Service

T—1010

11. Remove the cover from the stator plate to expose the breaker points. Completed ❑
12. Check the ignition cam for roughness. Completed ❑
13. Check the felt cam wiper. If the wiper is dry, place one drop of clean oil on the felt. If the system does not have a felt wiper, a special cam lubricating grease can be used sparingly. Completed ❑
14. Check the spring steel of the point assembly for evidence of excessive heat or weakness. Completed ❑
15. Check the contact points for wear. If they are pitted or burned, the condenser may be faulty. Completed ❑
16. If necessary, replace the points and the condenser. Completed ❑

Condenser Continuity Tests Using an Ohmmeter

17. Set the meter to read ohms. Completed ❑
18. Touch the ends of the test leads together and adjust the meter to read zero. Completed ❑
19. Disconnect the condenser wire. Completed ❑
20. Connect one lead to the condenser wire and ground the second test lead to the engine. Completed ❑
21. If the ohmmeter reads zero, the condenser is shorted and should be replaced. Completed ❑

Condenser Capacity Test Using a Merc-O-Tronic Model 9800 (98,98A) Tester

22. If a Merc-O-Tronic 98 or 98A is used, plug the tester into a 110/120 volt outlet. (Model 9800 does not require 110/120 volts.) Completed ❑

23. Position the Selector Switch to position #4, Condenser Capacity. See **Figure 10-2.** To calibrate the meter:
    A. Clip the black and red test leads together. Completed ☐
    B. For Merc-O-Tronic 98 and 98A, depress the red button to set the meter to the top of the scale. For a 9800 model, turn the Meter Set knob to set the line on scale 4. Completed ☐
    C. Unclip the test leads. Completed ☐

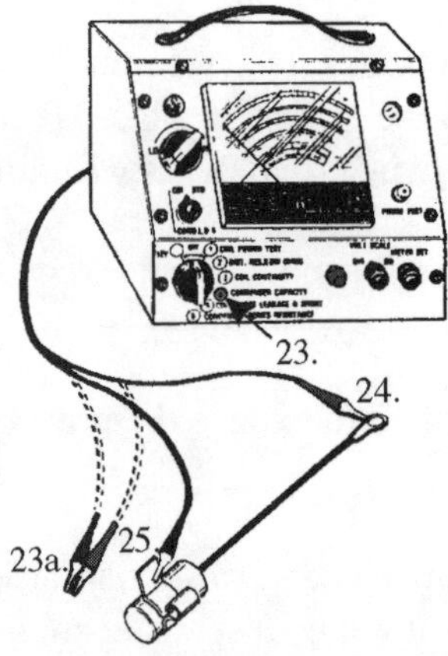

Figure 10-2. Condenser capacity test. Note that the numbers on the illustration correlate to the procedure numbers.

24. Connect the red test lead (alligator clip) to the condenser terminal. Completed ☐
25. Connect the black test lead (alligator clip) to the body of the condenser. Completed ☐
26. Read the value on scale 4. (On 98 and 98A models, the red button must be depressed during this test.) Completed ☐
27. If the microfarad value found in the test is not within the manufacturer's specifications, replace the condenser. Completed ☐

Coil Continuity Test Using an Ohmmeter

T—1335

If the engine failed the spark test and is not improved with new points and condenser, you should perform a coil test. Find the service manual coil winding resistances for the make and model engine at hand. If the coil does not meet manufacturer's specifications, it should be replaced.

28. Set the ohmmeter to the R × 100 or R × 1000 range and zero the meter as described in step 16 of this job. Completed ☐
29. Disconnect the primary and secondary coil wires. Completed ☐
30. Connect one test lead to the coil's high tension lead and the second lead to the coil's ground wire. Completed ☐
31. The meter reading may range from several hundred ohms to several thousand ohms. Refer to the service manual for specifications. Completed ☐
32. Remove the test lead from the high tension wire and connect it to the coil's primary wire. Completed ☐
33. Set the ohmmeter to its lowest resistance range. Completed ☐

Name ______________________________

34. If the meter reads zero, there is continuity in the primary coil. Completed ❑

35. If the meter reads infinite resistance in either test, the coil is faulty and must be replaced. Completed ❑

Coil Power Test Using a Merc-O-Tronic Model 9800 (98, 98A) Tester

The coil power test can be performed with the coil mounted on the engine. Isolation of the coil leads can be made by placing a piece of cardboard between the breaker points or by separating the coil primary lead, ground lead, and condenser lead.

Never perform this test without the spark plug high-tension lead attached to the tester's large red lead.

36. The ignition selector switch on the 9800 tester must be in the *Std.* position, **Figure 10-3.** (If 98 or 98A tester is used, a 55-980 adapter must be used.) Completed ❑

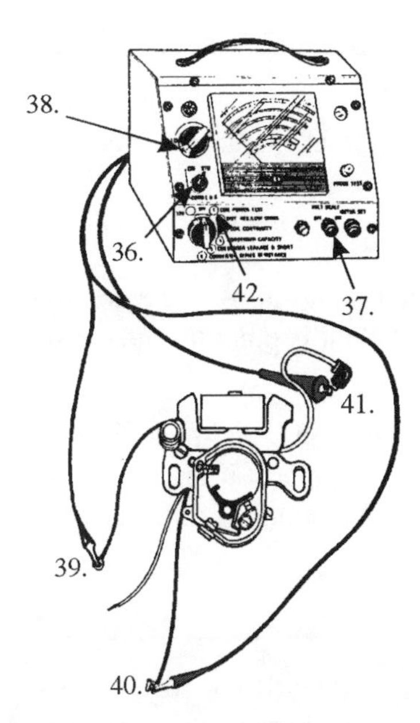

Figure 10-3. *Coil power test. Note that the numbers on the illustration correlate to the procedure numbers.*

37. Place the Volt Scale knob in the *off* position. Completed ❑

38. Place the *Lo-Hi* knob in the lowest possible position. Completed ❑

39. Connect the black test lead (alligator clip) to the primary ground lead or to the stator plate. Completed ❑

40. Connect the red test lead (alligator clip) to the primary coil lead. Completed ❑

41. Connect the large red test lead (alligator clip) to the terminal of the spark plug wire. Completed ❑

42. Turn the selector switch to the *Coil Power Test # 1* position. Completed ❑

43. Slowly turn the *Lo-Hi* knob clockwise and note the value on scale 1. When the meter reads the operating range for a particular winding (refer to coil manufacturer's specifications), stop turning the knob. The 5mm gap should fire steadily. Completed ❑

44. If the spark plug does not fire, or if the spark is weak or intermittent, replace the coil unit. Completed ❑

Setting Ignition Timing in Breaker Point Systems

45. Set the breaker point gap to amount specified in service manual.
    A. Rotate the crankshaft until the point arm is resting on the high side of the ignition cam. Completed ❑
    B. Loosen the screw on the movable point and insert a feeler gauge of proper thickness. Completed ❑
    C. Tighten the screw and recheck the gap. Completed ❑

46. Refer to the manufacturer's specifications for setting and measuring piston height in the cylinder. Turn the crankshaft forward until the piston reaches the correct height. Completed ❑

If the piston accidentally passes the specified height, continue to turn the crankshaft forward until the piston is returned to the correct height. Never reverse the direction of the crankshaft.

---

47. Disconnect the leads from the point terminal, reinstall the nut, and tighten it up. Connect one lead of a continuity light or an ohmmeter to the point terminal. Connect the other lead to a good ground. Completed ❑

48. Loosen the bolts holding the stator plate. Completed ❑

49. Hold the stator plate down while rotating it until the continuity light or ohmmeter indicates a break in the circuit. At this point torque the stator bolts. This completes the timing adjustment. Completed ❑

50. After points are replaced and the engine is retimed, clean the points with a lint-free paper. The engine will not run properly if the points are not correctly set or if they are coated with even a small amount of oil or dirt. Completed ❑

51. Replace the cover on the point box. Completed ❑

Some engines have timing marks on the crankshaft and camshaft gears. These engines must be running at recommended RPM with the point cover removed to time the ignition. A timing light (strobe light) must be aimed through the timing hole. The breaker point assembly is adjusted until the timing marks are in alignment. Lock the point assembly and check again with a timing light. Stop the engine and cover the point assembly.

Flywheel Installation

T—1415

52. Install a new key in the crankshaft keyway and install the flywheel. Torque the retaining nut to specifications. Completed ❑

53. Flywheels with external coils and magnets must have the proper air gap between the magnets and the coil laminations. With the coil-mounting screws loosened, place the correct air gap gauge between the flywheel and the coil. Completed ❑

Name ________________________________

54. Press the coil to the gauge and torque the screws to specifications. Completed ❑

55. Remove air gap gauge and rotate the flywheel to make sure no high spots contact the coil laminations. Completed ❑

Internal coils do not have air gap adjustment.

Solid State Pulse Transformer Test Using Merc-O-Tronic Model 79 Tester

56. Insert the test leads into the *Test Leads* jacks. See **Figure 10-4.** 

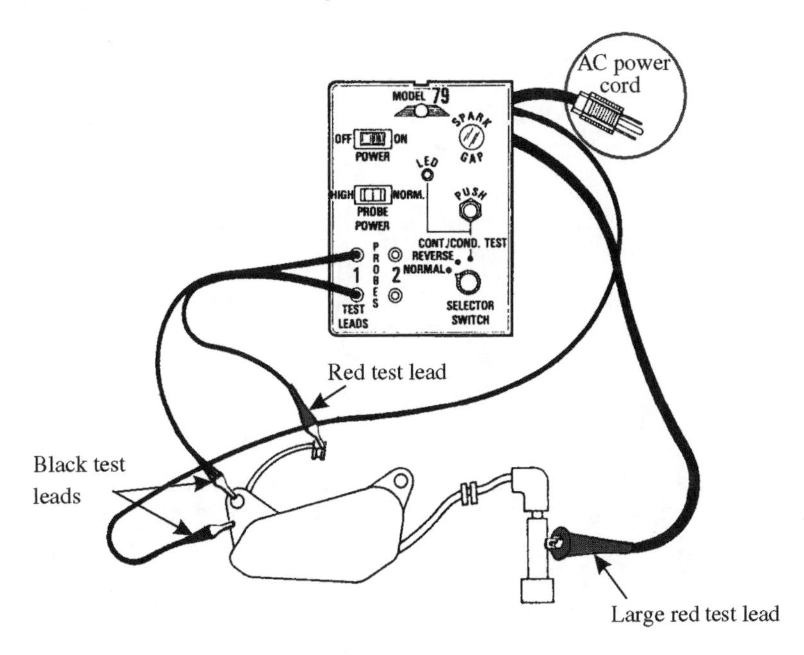

Figure 10-4. *Solid-state pulse transformer test.*

57. Connect the black test lead to the coil primary ground. Completed ❑

58. Connect the red test lead to the coil positive primary wire. Completed ❑

59. Connect the large red test lead to the high tension wire (use adapter if needed). Completed ❑

60. Connect the single black test lead from the analyzer to the coil primary ground wire. Normally, both black test leads will be connected in the same place. Completed ❑

61. Place the tester's selector switch in the *Normal* position. Completed ❑

62. Turn the power on. Completed ❑

63. Push the probe power switch to *Normal.* Completed ❑

64. A strong, steady spark should occur across the spark gap. Completed ❑

65. If the spark is faint, intermittent, or does not occur at all, the pulse transformer is defective and must be replaced. Completed ❑

Solid State Ignition System Test Using a Merc-O-Tronic Model 9800 (98, 98A) Tester and a CD 55-700 Adapter

66. If using a model 9800 tester, turn the ignition selector switch to the *Std.* position. Completed ❑

67. Attach a lead from the ignition coil terminal to the terminal on the ignition unit. See **Figure 10-5.** Completed ❑

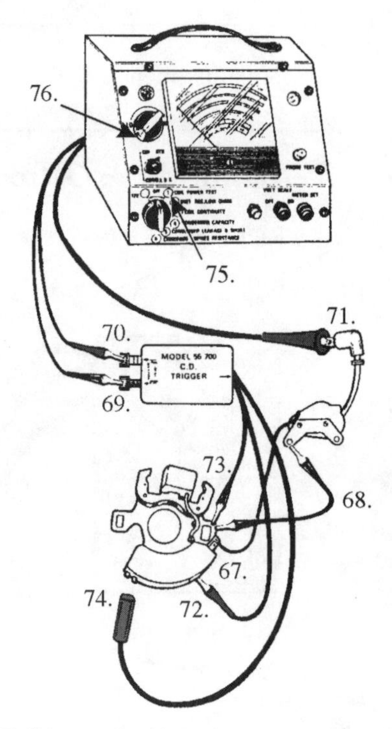

Figure 10-5. *Solid-state ignition system test. Note that the numbers on the illustration correlate to the procedure numbers.*

68. Attach a jumper lead from the ignition mounting plate to the ignition coil mounting plate. Completed ❑

69. Connect the black test lead (alligator clip) to the black terminal on the CD 55-700 unit. Completed ❑

70. Connect the red test lead (alligator clip) to the red terminal on the CD 55-700 unit. Completed ❑

71. Connect the large red test lead from the tester to the spark plug terminal on the high tension lead. Completed ❑

72. Attach the CD 55-700 adapter red lead to the ground cut-off terminal on the ignition unit (not pictured, located on the backside of the ignition unit). Completed ❑

73. Attach the CD 55-700 adapter black lead to the ignition unit mounting plate. Completed ❑

74. Place the electro-magnetic triggering device near the trigger terminal of the ignition unit. Completed ❑

75. Position the selector switch to *Coil Power Test.* Completed ❑

76. Slowly turn the *Lo-Hi* current knob clockwise until the ignition unit fires when viewed through the spark gap window. Completed ❑

While the test is in progress, it may be necessary to move the triggering device to achieve proper alignment with the trigger on the ignition unit.

Name ____

Checking an Ignition Switch

77. Disconnect the ground wire from the ground terminal on the engine. Completed ❑

78. Connect a test lamp between the ground wire and ground, as shown in **Figure 10-6.** Completed ❑

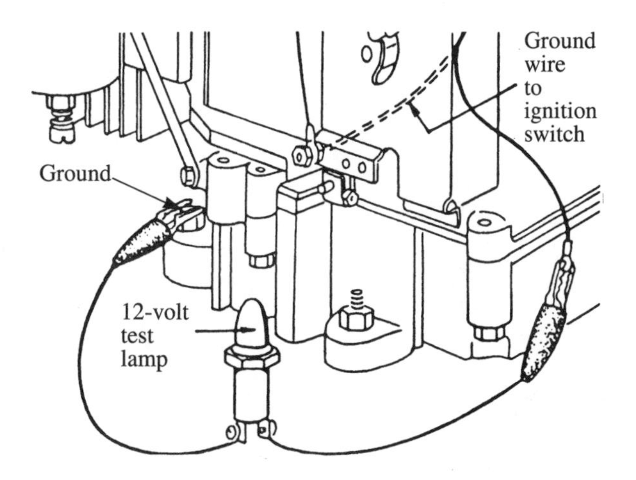

Figure 10-6. *Ignition switch test hookup.*

To prevent the engine from starting during this test, short the spark plug wire to ground.

79. Actuate the switch a minimum of 50 times. If the test lamp lights, even momentarily, the switch is defective and must be replaced. Completed ❑

Instructor's Initials ________________________

Date ________________________________

Fuel System Service

Name ______________________________

Date ____________________ Score________

Instructor ___________________________

Introduction

To maintain proper small engine operation, the fuel system must be serviced periodically. Fuel system service generally involves testing fuel system parts, replacing or rebuilding defective components, and making all necessary adjustments.

Objective

After successfully completing this job, you will be able to properly troubleshoot and service the fuel system on a small gasoline engine.

Materials and Equipment

To complete this job, you will need the following materials and equipment:

- Engine
- Clean shop rags
- Small parts containers
- Compressed air
- Pliers
- Combination, box, and open-end wrenches
- Socket set
- Screwdrivers
- Hammer
- Small chisel (1/8)
- Flat punch
- Safety fuel container
- Funnel
- Carburetor rebuild kit
- Float level gauge or proper size drill bit
- Carburetor cleaning solution and tank
- Respirator
- Rubber gloves
- Rubber apron
- Air filter element

Instructions

Before starting this job, review the material in Chapter 13, *Fuel System Service,* of the **Small Gas Engines** textbook. The **Small Gas Engines—Troubleshooting & Tune-up** video, available from Goodheart-Willcox Publisher, will also be helpful. As you complete each numbered step, place a check mark in the corresponding box. This will help you keep track of your progress. When you finish the job, ask your instructor to inspect your work and initial your completed job sheet.

Before performing this job, review all pertinent safety information in the text and discuss safety procedures with your instructor.

Procedure

Fuel System Service

T—1540

Note: Use extreme care when using or handling gasoline due to its high flammability. Store fuel only in approved gasoline containers. The fuel and oil mixture for two-cycle engines should be mixed in the proper ratio. Use only oil specified for two-cycle engines.

1. Drain the fuel from the tank. If there is a finger strainer inside the tank, unscrew and inspect the strainer. If the strainer is dirty or damaged, replace it. Completed ❑
2. Make sure the vent in the tank cap is open. A plugged vent can cause a vacuum to form in the tank, starving the engine of fuel. Completed ❑
3. Close the tank shut off valve and remove the inline fuel filter. If contaminants are found in the tank, or if the filter is blocked, replace the filter. When installing a new filter, make sure the arrow points toward the carburetor. Hose clamps must be in place. Completed ❑

Completed ❑

Carburetor Removal and Inspection

T—1805

There are many kinds of carburetors and it is essential that every part be replaced exactly as it was disassembled. If you don't have a carburetor service manual, take careful notes as you remove each apart.

4. Remove the fuel line from the carburetor. Completed ❑
5. Remove the carburetor from the engine. Completed ❑
6. Remove the mixture screws from the carburetor and inspect them for damage. Completed ❑
7. Inspect throttle and choke shafts for wear by moving them from side to side in their holes. Take note of the shape of the choke and throttle plates, as well as any marking on the plates. The choke and throttle plates must be reinstalled in the correct position and location. Remove the small screws and remove the plates. Also, remove the shafts. Completed ❑
8. Examine the carburetor body for damage. If damaged, replace the carburetor. Completed ❑

Completed ❑

Carburetor Disassembly

T—1855

9. Remove the fuel bowl by removing the bolt in the bottom of the bowl. Slide the hinge pin out to remove the float. The needle can then be removed from its seat. Do not lose the hinge pin or other small parts. Completed ❑

Name ______________________________

10. Examine the float for dents or leaks. Floats may be made of molded plastic, thin brass (soldered seams), or plastic foam. Examine the seat that contacts the needle. Completed ❑
11. Remove the needle valve and examine it. Completed ❑
12. Remove any welch plugs from the carburetor body. This procedure requires a small, narrow chisel and a hammer. Carefully drive the chisel through the welch plug and pry the plug out of the carburetor body. See **Figure 11-1.** Completed ❑

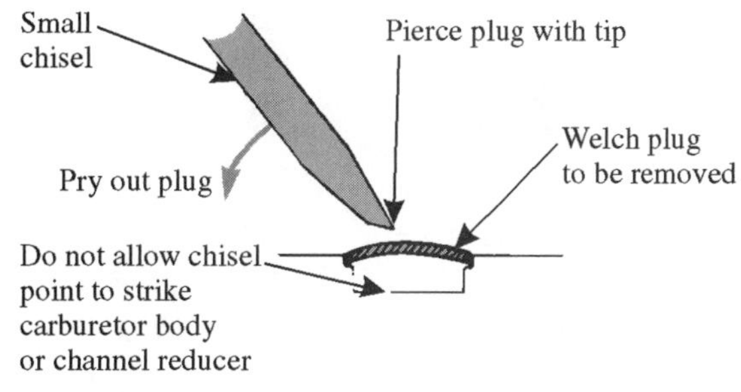

Figure 11-1. *When removing welch plugs, be careful not to damage the seat around the plug. A damaged seat may cause the new plug to leak. (Tecumseh Products Co.)*

13. Place the metal components that are to be reused in a parts basket and lower them slowly into carburetor cleaning solution. Allow them to soak for 15 to 20 minutes. Excessive time in the solution may cause etching and pitting of parts. Wear protective clothing such as a face mask, a rubber apron, and rubber gloves to avoid burns from the strong carburetor cleaning solution. Completed ❑
14. Remove the components from the cleaning solution and blow them dry with low pressure air. Make sure to blow out all internal passages. Completed ❑
15. Place the clean parts neatly on a clean, dry shop rags. Completed ❑

Carburetor Reassembly

T—2025

A full rebuild of the carburetor will require a rebuild kit. The kit will contain all the parts needed to do the job.

16. Install the welch plugs in the carburetor body with a flat pin punch that is slightly larger in diameter than the plug itself. Install the plug with the domed side up and set it with a light hammer blow. Do not dent the plug, **Figure 11-2.** Completed ❑

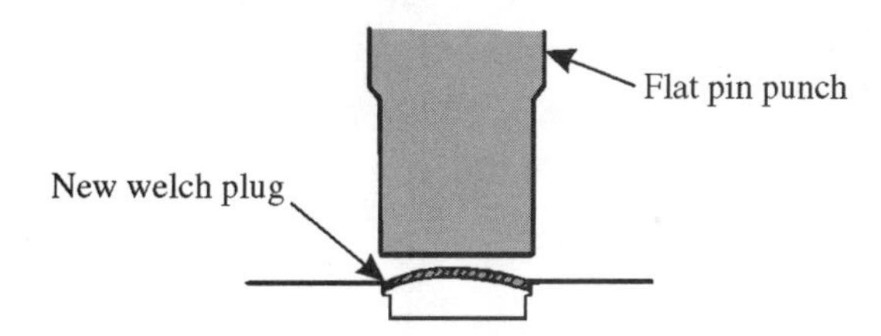

Figure 11-2. *New welch plugs are installed with a flat pin punch. Do not drive the center of the plug below the surface of the carburetor body. (Tecumseh Products Co.)*

17. Attach the needle valve to the float with a small spring. Completed ❑

18. Install the needle valve and float into the carburetor body. The needle valve must be positioned in the seat recess before the float hinge pin is installed. The float must move up and down freely. Completed ❑

19. Adjust the float height. Bend the float needle tab until the correct height is established. See **Figure 11-3.** Completed ❑

Figure 11-3. *A drill bit is a convenient tool for measuring float height. (Tecumseh Products Co.)*

20. Install the float bowl gasket and position the bowl so that the deep area is opposite the hinge. Use a new seal on the bowl nut and tighten the nut enough to set the seal. Completed ❑

21. Screw each needle valve (with springs and seals) into the carburetor. Your service manual will give instruction for presetting the needles for startup. Completed ❑

22. Install the carburetor on the engine with a new gasket. Completed ❑

23. Attach the linkage rods and fuel line. Completed ❑

24. Install a clean air filter element. Completed ❑

25. Make final adjustments of the idle speed needle and idle speed adjustment screw according to the manufacturer's recommendations. Completed ❑

Some carburetors do not have a high speed needle adjustment. The idle speed needle and rpm adjustment screw are the only adjustments necessary. Modern carburetors are preset and sealed at the factory for optimum performance at all speeds.

Instructor's Initials________________

Date ________________

SAMPLE TESTS

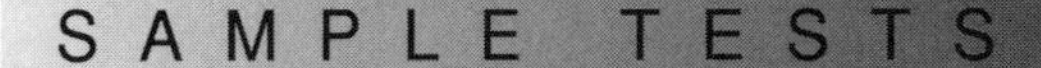

Outdoor Power Equipment Certification Examinations

The questions in the following sample tests are representative of the types of questions found on the Four-Stroke and Two-Stroke OPE Certification Examinations. These tests are intended to help those preparing for the exams to become familiar with the kinds of questions that might be asked. These tests are *not* intended to substitute for thorough study of the subject matter. The questions are similar, *not* a duplication of those on the OPE Certification Examinations.

Although the OPE Certification Examinations consist of 150 multiple choice questions, both sample tests contain only 15 questions.

OPE Sample Test

Four-Stroke Engines

Name______________________________

Date ________________ Period __________

Instructor______________________________

- Select the *best* answer for each question.

______ 1. Maintaining a well lighted, clean, and uncluttered shop:
   A. promotes safety.
   B. improves worker morale.
   C. improves efficiency.
   D. All of the above.

______ 2. A tap is used to:
   A. install piston wrist pins.
   B. repair damaged internal threads.
   C. chase external threads.
   D. drain oil from a crankcase.

______ 3. When using a hydraulic press, the best thing to use for a mandrel would be:
   A. a piece of ground tool steel.
   B. a proper size piece of cold rolled steel.
   C. a wrist pin from an old engine.
   D. an old socket.

______ 4. To measure crankshaft end play, the best tool to use would be a:
   A. depth micrometer.
   B. dial caliper.
   C. thickness gauge.
   D. dial indicator.

______ 5. Lead/acid and maintenance-free batteries produce:
   A. ac or dc current.
   B. direct current.
   C. alternating ac/dc.
   D. indirect current.

______ 6. A discharged battery, compared with a charged battery, will show a specific gravity reading that is:
   A. higher.
   B. the same.
   C. lower.

______ 7. Technician A says carburetors atomize fuel and combustion heat vaporizes it. Technician B says carburetors vaporize fuel and combustion heat atomizes it. Who is right?
A. Technician A is correct.
B. Technician B is correct.
C. Both technicians are correct.
D. Neither technician is correct.

______ 8. When the operator leaves a lawn mower, the blade must stop in:
A. 1 second.
B. 2 seconds.
C. 3 seconds.
D. 4 seconds.

______ 9. Excessively wide valve seats can cause:
A. warped valve stems.
B. indented valve seats.
C. burned margins.
D. carbon deposits on the valve seats.

______ 10. When draining oil it is best to:
A. drain the oil into a glass bottle.
B. pour kerosene into the crankcase before draining.
C. shake the engine to disperse the contaminants in the oil.
D. run the engine to thin the oil first.

______ 11. Fuels that are oxygenated:
A. reduce the amount of air needed by the engine.
B. increase the amount of air needed by the engine.
C. add oxygen molecules to the combustion process.
D. thin out the air-fuel mixture.

______ 12. Fuel volatility refers to:
A. evaporation heat.
B. octane rating.
C. vapor pressure.
D. viscosity.

______ 13. Vapor lock can occur when:
A. the fuel gets hot.
B. water gets in the fuel system.
C. the radiator overheats.
D. oil gets into the combustion chamber.

______ 14. Excessive piston ring end gap is a sign of:
A. overheating.
B. oil that is too thin.
C. worn rings.
D. a broken ring.

______ 15. If a valve is leaking, the next thing to do is:
A. check for burned head gasket.
B. remove valves.
C. check valve clearance.
D. check for carbon deposits in cylinder head.

OPE Sample Test

Two-Stroke Engines

Name______________________________

Date ____________________ Period ___________

Instructor_________________________

• Select the *best* answer for each question.

______ 1. A major advantage of a two-stroke engine over a four-stroke engine is that they:
A. are quieter.
B. start easier.
C. run in all positions.
D. run cooler.

______ 2. The metering diaphragm's main purpose in an all-position diaphragm carburetor is to:
A. control fuel flow through the carburetor.
B. pump fuel into the engine.
C. keep air from entering the fuel mixture.
D. keep the float bowl full.

______ 3. When the piston in a two-stroke engine travels downward from TDC, what is the first port to open?
A. Reed
B. Transfer
C. Bypass
D. Exhaust

______ 4. The best fuel/oil mixture for two-stroke engines is:
A. 30 parts of unleaded fuel to 1 part oil by volume.
B. 40 parts of leaded fuel to 1 part oil by weight.
C. recommended by engine manufacturer.
D. 50 parts unleaded fuel to 1 part oil.

______ 5. If you need to mix a fuel to oil ratio of 32:1, which of the following would be the proper proportion of fuel and oil to mix?
A. 1 gallon fuel with 1/2 pint of oil.
B. 2 gallons of fuel with 1 pint of oil.
C. 1 gallon of fuel with 2 pints of oil.
D. 1 gallon of fuel with 1 pint of oil.

______ 6. As elevation above sea level increases, engine horsepower will:
A. increase.
B. decrease.
C. not be affected.
D. exceed the manufactured limits.

______ 7. Cylinder head bolts should be removed with:
A. a socket wrench in a crisscross pattern.
B. an air wrench in a crisscross pattern.
C. an air wrench in a circular pattern.
D. a socket wrench in a circular pattern.

______ 8. An engine with a baffle, or deflector, on the crown would be:
A. rotary valve type.
B. loop scavenged.
C. cross scavenged.
D. transfer port type.

______ 9. The best tool to use to measure crankshaft end clearance would be a:
A. dial indicator.
B. dial caliper.
C. wire gauge.
D. Plastigage.

______ 10. In a CDI ignition system, what is charged by the trigger coil?
A. Diode
B. SCR
C. C-D module
D. Capacitor

______ 11. What supplies extra air-fuel mix between low- and high-speed throttle openings?
A. Transition/intermediate ports
B. Air bleeds
C. Diaphragm pump
D. Venturi pump

______ 12. Automatic variable ignition timing can:
A. make the engine run smoother.
B. keep the engine from overheating.
C. prevent overspeeding.
D. make starting easier.

______ 13. Cylinder head bolts:
A. are SAE NF threads.
B. are always the same length.
C. require a sealant on the threads.
D. require a torquing sequence when installing.

______ 14. Removing carbon after disassembling the engine helps to:
A. restore horsepower.
B. make engine run cooler.
C. increase valve life.
D. All of the above.

______ 15. Carburetor adjustment should be done by setting the:
A. high speed needle first.
B. idle speed needle first.
C. idle adjusting screw first.
D. The order does not matter.